WOMEN OF
MODERN SCIENCE

By EDNA YOST
Author of *Modern American Engineers*, etc.
Illustrated with photographs

The twentieth century has witnessed an ever increasing number of women assuming vital roles in the varied fields of modern science. *Women of Modern Science* presents a gallery of eleven portraits of gifted women, eight of them American born, who have already made outstanding contributions to research in the science to which they were dedicated. Included among them are Gerty Cori, the only American woman to be awarded the Nobel Prize, and Lise Meitner, one of the great pioneers in the study of atomic fission; Helen Hogg, astronomer; Elizabeth Russell, zoologist-geneticist; Rachel Brown, researcher in antibiotics; Chien Wu, nuclear physicist; Edith Quimby, radiologist; Jocelyn Crane, zoologist; Florence Van Straten, meteorologist; Gladys Emerson, biochemist; and Dorothea Rudnick, embryologist.

With the skill that she brought to such previous books as *Modern American Engineers*, Edna Yost personally interviewed and won the endorsement of each subject, except in two instances where it was impossible, to present a lucid and authoritative description of the work accomplished as well as a human story of the struggles that led to each achievement.

JACKET BY

Women of Modern Science

Women of Modern Science

By EDNA YOST

ILLUSTRATED
WITH PHOTOGRAPHS

DODD, MEAD & COMPANY
NEW YORK / 1959

To F B H
for a half-century
of friendship

Printed in the United States of America
by The Cornwall Press, Inc., Cornwall, N. Y.

925
Y

ACKNOWLEDGMENTS

THIS BOOK would not have been possible without the co-operation of the women whose sketches appear in it. They talked with me about their work and the years of their youth in which their lifework had been chosen. They provided me with reprints describing their scientific contributions, then read the sketches to detect errors even a conscientious layman may make in writing about science. Thus, though expressions of opinion are mine alone, scientific and biographical facts have been verified by each biographee.

Dr. Lise Meitner's sketch is an exception. To talk with her (in Copenhagen) was not possible. Thanks are due to Dr. Otto Hahn's book *New Atoms—Progress and Some Memories,* which gave me a more personal picture of Dr. Meitner's work than I found elsewhere. Especial thanks are due the distinguished physicist who read Dr. Meitner's sketch, and to Russell R. Yost, Jr., who read the manuscript before I cared—possibly dared—to have it submitted to the eminent scientist whose approval the publisher desired.

Nor did I speak personally with Dr. Gerty Cori, who died shortly after some preliminary correspondence. To

19171

Dr. Carl Cori, who later talked at length with me about his wife when I knew it was not easy for him, I am most deeply grateful. The spirit beneath his desire to have her life and work serve younger women who may work in science will be a shining memory in my own life always. To Dr. Alice Bernheim, friend of the Coris in whose home our interview took place, I am also indebted for warm personal glimpses into Gerty Cori's life.

In working up a long list of names from which my final selection of scientists was made, help came from Dr. Libbie H. Hyman and Dr. Florence B. Seibert, sketches of whose lives appear in my earlier *American Women of Science;* from Edith Newton; from headquarters' staffs in national scientific organizations; from college teachers and other individuals too numerous to mention here. So the book has been a co-operative undertaking in every sense of the word. Not the least part of that co-operation has come from the publisher who originated the idea for the book and his editor, Allen T. Klots, Jr., who never failed to come up with a constructive suggestion when it was needed.

PREFACE

◆◆

V ERY LITTLE biographical material is available about women who are scientists. Yet biography interests many readers, and science is a colorful background when presented in words and ideas a layman can understand. These brief sketches attempt to take advantage of this fact. Their background should be understandable, often exciting, to readers who know very little science.

A book of this kind offers an experience to its author over and above what is written into it. Of this experience, two aspects in particular may be interesting to readers. One of them, less cheerful than the other, may throw some light upon a question that troubles many thoughtful Americans today—the question concerning how to improve our educational system so that it will produce as many high-caliber scientists as we need.

In talking with scientists, both men and women, of other than American birth and early education, I found some who were outspoken in their conviction that young women possessing scientific talents in their own countries had one great advantage over similarly gifted young women in America. They had the good fortune of being able to grow up in an environment in which psychological freedom for recognizing and developing scientific talents exists for both sexes alike.

These scientists of other nationalities had been surprised, they told me, to find in America where so many more young women go to college than in the lands in which they had been born, an attitude that seemed to be based on an assumption that it is not so "natural" for a girl to possess scientific talents as for a boy. They felt this false assumption imposed certain penalties nonexistent in their own lands. This attitude, they continued, has deprived many of our gifted young people of true freedom of choice in the period when strong innate gifts are usually recognized and vocational choices made. The basic need of our educational system, so far as its adequacy for developing scientists is concerned, they urge, is an environment in which scientific talents may express themselves without meeting prejudices that make their possession and development less desirable to anyone.

This point of view impressed me more and more as I worked with the women whose biographical sketches appear in this book. Of the eight who were born in America, five had no intention of majoring in science when they entered college. Surely that is a high percentage in a group whose outstanding talents were undoubtedly in this realm. Three of those five had omitted physics and chemistry completely, and mathematics except for the minimum, from their high school curricula. Something in their environment had made it easy for these girls to remain in ignorance of their own high gifts and potentialities.

I was impressed still again when, in the course of my research, I came across another fact that made me wonder about the advantages and disadvantages of the American environment. Of the five women elected to membership in our National Academy of Sciences in the past twenty-five years, four were born and educated (through the first college degree period, at least) in other countries. Those countries are Austria, Russia, Germany, and China.

So much for the less cheerful aspects of an author's experience.

The heartening experience I want to share with readers is that many higher-level opportunities exist for young American women who want to become scientists. Academic work beyond a bachelor's degree is usually necessary for advancement to these higher levels of work but —and this is what I want to stress—many opportunities for scholarships and fellowships are available for college science majors of both sexes and limited financial means who need to earn a living as they study for their Ph.D.'s. Certainly more such opportunities are available to women today than existed some sixteen years ago when I was doing research for an earlier book of biographical sketches of women scientists. Were I a young woman today with the requisite natural qualifications, I would not hesitate to aim at a doctorate in any science in the belief that I could finance my own way during the postgraduate period and that I would find opportunities for advancement later.

Finally, an explanation of the way selection of biographees for this book was made.

The publisher asked me to find a group of women whose scientific work covered a variety of fields of interest to younger women thinking of science as a possible life work. No attempt would be made to determine the "best" woman scientist in each field. (Rarely is such determination possible anyway.) We agreed that we should have scientists of different ages, some with their work nearly finished and others with, possibly, their most important work still ahead of them. Each person's work, however, must already have earned genuine respect in its own field. In short, for our Table of Contents we wanted good scientists with two qualifications: First, they had to be women; second, these women had to have achieved high standing as scientists among leaders in their fields, of both sexes. To find them I would need help from many qualified sources, but final choices would always be mine.

The next step was more difficult. I had to convince these women one by one that the project we had in mind warranted their co-operation. The fact that each was a scientist of achievement and each was busy would be no drawback, for the bigger and busier the person, the more likely he, or she, is to give help if convinced an undertaking is worth while and cannot be done properly without co-operation. The biggest hurdle I had to leap was that so many scientists not only do not want but often have an aversion to anything that seems like personal publicity and, unfortunately, the term "biographical sketch" is often applied today to fictionalized misrepresentations that are mainly personal publicity.

In each case we came to agreement when it was

clear between us that each understood the difference between publicity and biography and that my aim was
truthful biography with stress on scientific achievement.
If each would help me show the successive steps by
which an embryo scientist had found her special interest
and her way ahead in it, I promised to produce a book
that would fill a recognized biographical need.

Here, then, is the result of that co-operation—a book
about women of achievement in science. And here is an
author who has had a great personal privilege in meeting
and working with a group of "big" human beings who,
without making her feel small, have gently stretched her
mind to greater comprehension of the age in which we
are living.

—EDNA YOST

New York City
January 1959

CONTENTS

● ●

ILLUSTRATIONS

Lise Meitner with a group of Science Talent Search winners

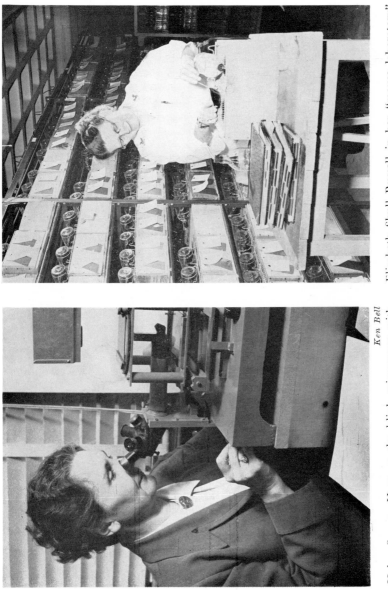

Ken Bell

Helen Sawyer Hogg at the blink microscope with which she has found many new variable stars

Elizabeth Shull Russell in her "mouse laboratory"

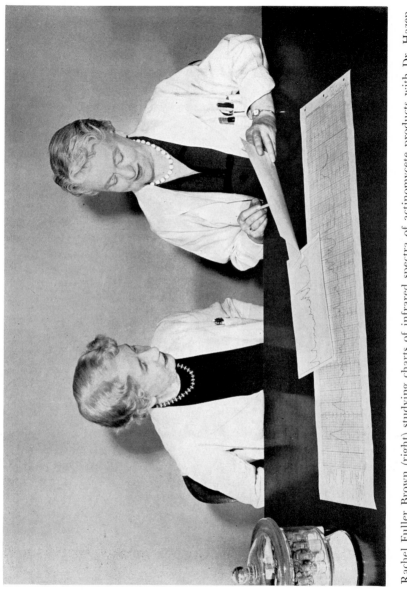

Rachel Fuller Brown (right) studying charts of infrared spectra of actinomycete products with Dr. Hazen

Courtesy of Westinghouse

Chien Shiung Wu with winners of the Science Talent Search in Washington

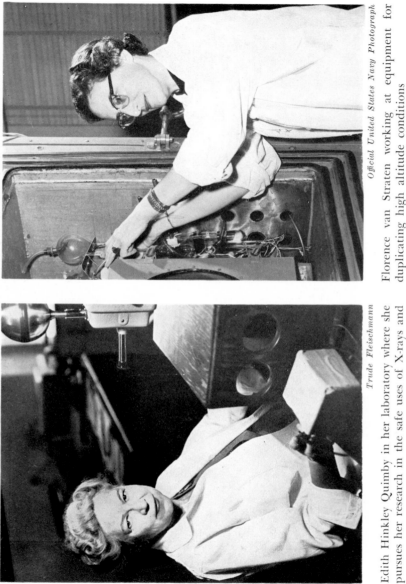

Florence van Straten working at equipment for duplicating high altitude conditions

Edith Hinkley Quimby in her laboratory where she pursues her research in the safe uses of X-rays and radioactive materials

Jocelyn Crane ready to dig for the only species of fiddler crabs in West Africa

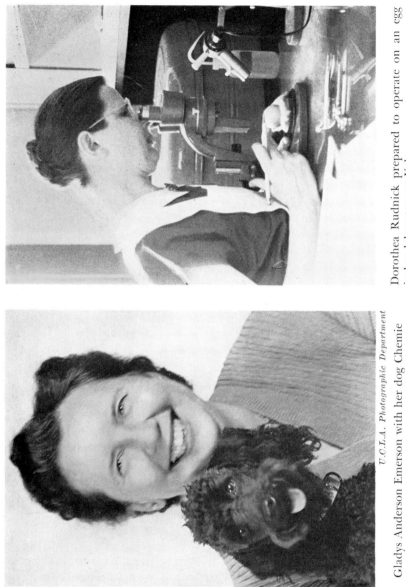

Gladys Anderson Emerson with her dog Chemie

Dorothea Rudnick prepared to operate on an egg in her laboratory at Yale

GERTY THERESA CORI

(1896–1957)

●●●

Austrian-born co-winner, with her distinguished husband, of a Nobel Prize in science, the only American
woman who has achieved this high honor

THERE ARE THREE Nobel Prizes in science, one in chemistry, one in physics, and a third in physiology and medicine. Awarded annually since 1901 without regard for
race, creed, or nationality, these prizes are regarded as
the world's highest awards in science. If contributions
in any field in any year do not, in the belief of the
board charged with administering the awards, warrant
the honor, the prize in that field is withheld.

Three times a husband and wife team of scientists has
been chosen to receive one of these awards. The three
women on these teams are the only women who have as yet
received a Nobel Prize in science.* In 1947 the honor

* Marie Curie, who shared the Nobel Prize in Physics with her husband
in 1903, later received the Prize in Chemistry alone. She is not only the only
woman to receive a Nobel Prize in science alone, but the only person who
has ever been chosen twice for a Nobel award.

1

came to America for the first time when half the Nobel Prize in Physiology and Medicine was awarded to Carl and Gerty Cori of the Washington University School of Medicine in St. Louis. Though Austrians by birth, the Coris had become Americans by choice soon after their graduation from medical school in Prague. As Americans they had found opportunity to do all the research that led to their award, and as American citizens for almost twenty years they received their distinguished honor.

This is the story of a girl called Gerty Theresa Radnitz, who grew into the woman who earned her full share of that prize. Her life and work became so closely knit with her husband's that to speak of one without the other is impossible except when telling of their lives before they met and began to work together in medical school. One, at least, of those early years was a particularly difficult one for Gerty Radnitz. Unless, as a sixteen-year-old, she had been willing to buckle down to unusually hard work, she might have missed out on one of the fullest, richest, happiest lives a woman has ever been privileged to live.

Hers was a life of many facets, each of them of importance in developing her into the maturely rounded human being she became. As a wife and mother she enjoyed a woman's satisfactions in the happy home she helped create. As a dedicated scientist she found deep satisfactions in difficult laboratory problems to which she brought rigid intellectual discipline and creative imagination. As a warm and lovable human being she cherished and was cherished by friends of many creeds and nationalities. As a woman who endured ten years of illness without being warped by the physical limitations it eventually put upon her, she grew in human stature and understanding by her acceptance of it. She lived to see her contributions to humanity's health and illness problems establish their enduring significance and receive high scientific acclaim. The rewarding experiences life held for her were surely beyond anything she could have anticipated when she undertook to master the difficulties that stood between her and her desire to study medicine when she was sixteen.

To begin at the beginning, Gerty Radnitz was born in Prague (a city that was then in Austria), where her father was the manager of several sugar refineries. Like most girls of her social group, she went, after private tutoring up to the age of ten, to a girls' school. It was a good school as such institutions were rated in Austria at that time. Its aim was to fit young women of good families for life by developing, mainly, their social and cultural graces. Since certain innate intellectual abilities did not fall within the scope of these graces, science and mathematics had very little place in its curriculum. Their absence did not bother Gerty Radnitz at the moment. She enjoyed the studies that were offered, and her teachers surely found she possessed gifts in the social graces that were not hard to cultivate. They were far too naturally a part of her ever to become smothered beneath scientific achievement in later years. Dr. Cori's graciousness was always one of her charms.

Yet Gerty Radnitz was not a girl who could long accept limitations of her fuller intellectual development. By the time she was sixteen and ready to graduate from the school her parents had chosen for her, she had decided—

possibly influenced to a degree by an uncle who was a professor of pediatrics at a medical school—to study medicine. Inquiries revealed that, before she could be accepted at a medical school, she needed eight years of Latin (of which she had had none at all), five more years of mathematics than she had had, plus physics and chemistry. All this work could be done at a Gymnasium, a type of school where students were preponderantly boys but where she could be accepted if she proved able to do the work. The medical school curriculum, she knew, would take six years after she was able to enter upon it. To one of her years it must have seemed as if she would be a doddering grayhead before she could get her medical degree. Being Gerty Radnitz, however, she made up her mind to enjoy a summer's vacation after her graduation, then get the pre-med work over with as quickly as possible. She was going to be a doctor!

Vacationing in the Tyrol that summer, she met a man who was a teacher at the Realgymnasium in Tetschen. When her new acquaintance heard what Gerty's problems and plans were, he suggested one day, "Then why not let me help you get started in Latin this summer?" The response was affirmative, and vacationers saw less and less of the attractive brown-eyed girl with the mass of reddish-brown hair who had been specializing on a summer of fun before getting down to work in earnest that fall. By the time her vacation was over, Gerty Radnitz had worked off three years of Latin and was ready to try to keep up the pace with the remaining five years of it if she could.

She enrolled at the Realgymnasium in Tetschen that

fall with one purpose—to master with all possible speed all the courses needed to prepare her for entrance examinations for the medical school. In one year she had accomplished this seemingly impossible task, which included mathematics through calculus. Undoubtedly her intellectual capacities and ability to discipline herself were of a high order. She passed the examinations. All her life she spoke of them as "the hardest examinations I was ever called upon to take."

The University of Prague, whose medical school she entered just after her eighteenth birthday, was one of the most ancient and distinguished of European universities. At that time Charles Ferdinand, as the university was called, was divided into two branches, one of which was Czech and the other, German. Miss Radnitz enrolled at the Medical College of the German University as, happily, did a tall blue-eyed youth called Carl Cori, whose eighteenth birthday was still a few months ahead. Somewhere not far along in their student days these two met. In due time they teamed up for some laboratory research in biochemistry, a subject to which Gerty Radnitz had been strongly attracted in her first year of work in it. She and Carl Cori enjoyed working together; they enjoyed seeing the results of their collaboration on an immunological study in print, bearing both their names.

They had also discovered they enjoyed each other outside the laboratory. It was fun climbing the Austrian Alps together, it was happiness to swim or skate or ski together. Needless to say they fell in love. Surely no one who ever met them could long wonder why. They were graduated with their M.D.'s in the spring of 1920 and married before the summer was over.

While they had been in medical school, World War I had been fought, and won or lost, depending upon the angle from which one viewed it. For Austria it had been devastatingly lost. The university they had entered was no longer in Austria. Prague had become the capital of a newly formed country, Czechoslovakia. Need existed for doctors who wanted to practice medicine, but the future did not look promising to two young doctors who definitely preferred biochemical research to medical practice. Dr. Carl found opportunity for this type of research in Vienna after their graduation. Dr. Gerty became a member of the staff of the Children's Hospital in that same city. Using the facilities at hand, she, too, was able to do some research in addition to carrying on her hospital duties. Papers describing her studies of thyroid and spleen appeared in a scientific journal. But neither she nor her husband felt Europe offered adequate opportunities for the type of research to which they wanted to devote their time. America became a land of promise in their minds. They sought a way to reach it.

Two years after their graduation Carl Cori secured a position as a biochemist at the New York State Institute for the Study of Malignant Diseases in Buffalo. He came to America alone. Within a few months he had found an opening for his wife as an assistant pathologist at this same institute. She came, passed civil-service examinations necessary for such jobs, and a few years later received an appointment as assistant biochemist. In this position it would not be necessary for her to spend so

much time investigating pathological conditions—a welcome change because Gerty Cori was always primarily
interested in learning more and more about the function-
ing of bodies in health than in illness.

So it was in America that these two were able to re-
sume joint research as they had first worked together in
medical school. Since that time (1922) the great majority (though not all) of the scientific papers signed by one
Cori bears the name of the other Cori, too. And, though
each received awards and honors in which the other did
not share, the highest award of all, the Nobel Prize, quite
justly came to them as a team of scientists whose greatest
contributions were made in work they had done together.

Early biochemical researches in Buffalo, as might be
expected from the name of the institute providing them
with facilities for work, were on various aspects of abnormal growths in the human body. Since all body growth,
normal and abnormal, is created out of the foods we
eat, the chemical processes (called metabolism) occurring
as elements in foods are transformed into living body-
building materials caught the interest of the biochemi-
cally minded Coris. Results of some of their early studies
on the metabolism of tumors proved of interest not only
to scientists concerned with abnormal growths but to
those interested in the metabolism of normal growth.
For the Coris this early work stimulated desire to investigate these processes further.

Adding interest and suggesting a direction for further
research was the fact that insulin had recently been discovered. Insulin is a protein (of the group called hormones) manufactured in normal bodies and used by them

to control utilization of carbohydrates (that is, the sugars and starches in our food) during metabolic processes. To the physician in medical practice the discovery of insulin provided an effective tool for controlling diabetes, a disease that often occurs when the body does not utilize carbohydrates properly. To two physicians working as biochemists, it offered a new tool for finding out more about some of the many not-yet-understood chemical processes going on constantly throughout the whole of the human body, particularly as they handle the carbohydrates in our food.

Medical and physiological training had given these two biochemists an excellent background to bring to biochemical research involving the whole body. The Institute for the Study of Malignant Diseases proved ready to give them adequate means and complete freedom for undertaking it. Throughout all her later life Gerty Cori spoke with gratitude of the "fine generosity" and "wonderful opportunities" she and her husband had found in America for the type of research to which they were drawn. Here at the Buffalo institute was an early example of what she meant.

Centering their investigations upon the chemical processes involved in the body's use of sugars, the Coris fed white rats a known quantity of sugar, giving insulin to some but not to others. The animals were then put into respiratory chambers where determinations could be made showing how much of the sugar was oxidized. In due time their bodies were analyzed for carbohydrate. Using these and other techniques, the Coris were able to learn that about half of the absorbed sugar had been converted to glycogen and stored in this form in liver and muscles, that some of the sugar had been converted to fat and stored as fat, and the rest burned (oxidized) to carbon dioxide and water.

The results of their planned feeding and analyses of experimental animals showed that insulin decreased the amount of sugar stored in the liver and increased its utilization otherwise. This was valuable new knowledge for physicians in their treatment of diabetic patients. Further experiments, in which various forms of sugar were used and hormones other than insulin were administered, gave other valuable insights into the body's hidden chemical processes. Eventually they revealed that glycogen deposited in the muscles produces lactic acid, which the blood stream carries to the liver; there it is changed to liver glycogen that in turn gives rise to blood glucose which is later transformed into the muscle glycogen, with which the process started. This ever-recurring process in our bodies is known as the "Cori cycle." It adds considerably to man's knowledge of body metabolism.

In 1931 an offer came which was to give the Coris greater opportunities than were possible at the Buffalo institute. Washington University in St. Louis asked Dr. Carl Cori to accept a professorship on its staff, and Dr. Gerty Cori to become a fellow and research associate. They accepted, and an appointment as an associate professor of biochemistry came to Gerty Cori later. Rank as a full professor was attained shortly before the Nobel Prize award. But teaching, except for the teaching of graduate students, never became a most important part of her lifework. Research was the aspect of science to which she was truly dedicated. "The unforgotten moments of my life," she once said, "are those rare ones which come after years of plodding work when the veil over nature's secret seems suddenly to lift and what was dark and chaotic appears in a beautiful light and pattern."

At St. Louis she had from the beginning freedom to work in the laboratory as an equal with her husband. Their method was to determine and set out upon the investigation they would pursue next. They talked over problems as they arose, decided what was to be done about them, and divided the tasks between them. Then, as each worked at his own tasks, alone or with student or other assistants, he—and she—would check and correlate with the other all along the way. Some of the hours Dr. Carl gave to his teaching and administrative duties Dr. Gerty devoted to the home that meant so much to both of them—a home where plants and flowers flourished under Dr. Gerty's green thumb, where good music and good pictures were provided for and appreciated, and where, a few years after their arrival in St. Louis, a small son appeared to make a Cori threesome out of what, for fourteen years of marriage, had been only a twosome.

Young Tommy's appearance scarcely interrupted his mother's work, so intelligently co-ordinated was the research work with home and maternal duties during pregnancy and the years in which their small son needed constant attention. Dr. Carl Cori had much to do with the way in which his wife's work continued at this period of their lives, as well as in later years when she worked during periods of illness.

The work they determined to embark upon in St. Louis had continuity with the work done at Buffalo even though its emphasis and direction were changed. As has been mentioned, the Coris had shown that glycogen in the body underwent a series of chemical changes during the Cori cycle. Some of these changes were due to proteins known as enzymes which, like hormones, are also manufactured in normal bodies and used in their chemical processes. Interest in the changes occurring in glycogen during these processes made the Coris determine to investigate enzyme systems in an attempt to understand the transformations occurring in glycogen. These investigations led to a brilliant series of fundamental discoveries.

Very little was known about enzymes at that time. There is still all too little known about them. It is believed that, in inducing chemical changes in our bodies, an enzyme acts as a catalyzer and that each specific enzyme usually acts upon only one specific substance. Enzymes are extremely complex in their structure—a fact that makes them extremely difficult to work with. For this and other reasons, describing the Cori work on them to a layman would be a difficult and in the end, possibly, an unrewarding task. Some of the results of that work, however, can be stated in a way that can give the layman an idea of it, at least. For example:

Starting with some minced, thoroughly washed frog muscle, and using established techniques with others of their own imaginative contrivance, they produced, isolated, identified, and then created synthetically a hitherto unknown sugar phosphate known as the "Cori ester."

They discovered two new enzymes, phosphorylase and phosphoglucomutase, words that suggest the complexity of enzyme structure to the layman. They tracked down the enzymes that acted specifically on glycogen during the metabolic processes of the Cori cycle, and identified catalytic effects in producing the changes in its chemical structure. Eventually—and this was a far more difficult task than a simple statement of results may make it appear—they discovered the structure of the glycogen molecule. In the process of doing her share of the work in all this, Gerty Cori differentiated four different types of glycogen storage disease. Later, (1953) she delivered one of the Harvey Lectures before that society in New York, describing this work as it had progressed at that time.

In recognition of their work—"for their discovery of how glycogen is catalytically converted"—Carl and Gerty Cori received half of the Nobel Prize in Physiology and Medicine for 1947. The other half went to Dr. Bernardo A. Houssay, an Argentinean physiologist who had demonstrated the effect of the pituitary gland secretions on the body's use of sugar.

A Nobel Prize in any field stamps the work it honors as having originality and significance. In the case of the two Coris the scientific achievements that were so honored are only a part of their contributions to problems affecting illness and health. Of equal significance, possibly, was the fact that their laboratory in St. Louis had become a center which attracted scores of first-class scientists interested in carbohydrate metabolism. Many papers on this subject have been published as a result of the stimulating atmosphere of this one research center, and their end is far from reached. It may be that work originating there will throw sufficient light on some of the diseases common to middle and later life that these illnesses will be lessened in frequency and yield to new treatments as they are better understood. If, as some medical men believe, diseases of kidney, liver, heart, and blood vessel walls often occur as a result of overconsumption of foods that load our bodies with more fat and carbohydrates than they can handle successfully while depriving them of other types of foods that would provide nutrients essential for better metabolism, work emanating from the Washington University laboratory may stimulate greater interest in the better eating habits that would help prevent these diseases.

To her friends it was a tragedy that Gerty Cori, even before she accompanied her husband to Stockholm in 1947 to receive her high honor from Sweden's King Gustavus V, should have been attacked by a disease science has not yet learned how to handle successfully. But it was an inspiration to them to see how she refused, for more than ten years, to let it stop her work. Gone, eventually, were the days when she and Carl could pick up their skates or tennis racquets for some exercise before going back to the laboratory, or start out together to scale a peak in the Rockies and recapture memories of youthful days when they had climbed the Alps and all the future lay ahead of them. There was still the garden in St. Louis where Carl cared for the vegetables and Gerty, for the flowers. Young Tommy was supposed to develop a helpful interest in the weeds as he grew older, though whether he did or not is quite another matter.

The wide seats beneath the curtainless windows in her dining and living rooms were a garden in themselves for her in periods when Dr. Gerty had to spend more time at home, periods from which she recovered, at first, so that she could go about her laboratory work as usual and off to meetings where her presence was needed. Even during illness she continued the reading that was a life-long habit. Her interests ranged far beyond science. Biography, history, and the current events that make history were the subjects of the books she read with regularity, two or three of them a month. She was an unusually well-informed woman in any group in which she found herself. Art, as well as science, she saw as one of the glories of the human mind. She found no conflict between them.

And always there were friends—friends who were to marvel that, even as her strength became more and more limited and every ounce of energy increasingly precious to the work to which she was dedicated, she seemed incapable of withholding herself from people whose problems she knew. Her last letter, unfinished at the time of her death, was to a friend whose husband was ill, expressing the hope that he was or would soon be better. In a "this I believe" credo written during the years of her illness, she said, "Honesty, which stands mostly for intellectual integrity, courage, and kindness are still the virtures I admire most." Then she added that her emphasis on these virtures had shifted somewhat over the years, so that kindness seemed more important to her than it had in her youth. Kindness, including the ability to listen in human sympathy to another's problems with the desire to help—if she could—was a virtue her friends found in her, and it did not desert her in the years of illness.

Honors came to Gerty Cori as they have come to few women scientists, most of them after the Nobel award. She became the fourth woman member of our National Academy of Sciences in 1947, eight years after her husband's election to that body. The year before the Nobel award she shared the Midwest Award in Science with her husband and, after the Nobel Prize, his second Sugar Research Prize. Honorary doctorates in science, sometimes with and sometimes without her husband's sharing in the honor, came to her from Boston and Yale universities, Smith College, the University of Rochester, and Columbia. She shared with her husband the Squibb Award in Endocrinology in 1947 and the next year received the Garvan Gold Medal, an honor reserved for women only. In 1950 came the Borden Award of the Association of American Medical Colleges and an appointment by President Truman to the board of the newly established National Science Foundation. This appointment, retained for the remainder of her life, involved much work and frequent trips to meetings in Washington.

Gerty Cori believed it was her good fortune to have had the type of education available in Europe and then to have been able to use it on opportunities available in America. These two advantages, she believed, had been basic to the success of her own and her husband's work —work that had been recorded in some 150 to 200 scientific papers at the time of her death. Other advantages she brought to it, too, advantages accruing from innate gifts waiting only to be developed into assets for biochemical research. "She was a woman who always knew a fact from a fancy" is the way one of her friends described her as Carl Cori nodded in affirmation—Carl Cori, who knew better than anyone else how valuable that characteristic had been in their four decades of companionship and some thirty-five years of active scientific collaboration.

LISE MEITNER

(1878–   )

●●

Austrian-born physicist whose contributions in solving
the problems of atomic fission played an important role
in tapping a new source of energy for man's use

Lise meitner's scientific achievements are in a field to
which comparatively few American women seem as yet
to have been strongly attracted—that of physics. To explain this seeming lack of interest, the claim is often made
here in America that "girls aren't good at math or
physics." Yet physics is a science in which some women
have actually shown outstanding ability. Europe has produced two of them—women whose contributions are ac-
knowledged to be of the highest rank when judged by the
world's most distinguished physicists.

The names of these two women are Marie Curie and
Lise Meitner. They helped revolutionize nineteenth-century physics and its concepts. Their names stand high in
any truthful record of the achievements that eventually

17

brought the use of atomic energy and power to reality.

Fewer people know the facts about Lise Meitner's contributions to this achievement than know about Marie Curie, who was awarded the Nobel Prize in Physics in 1903. Mme. Curie shared this prize with two men, one of them her husband. But many people do not know that, in accomplishing their pioneer work in radioactivity that resulted in the discovery of radium and its isolation from uranium ore—the investigations that brought the Nobel Prize—it was Marie Curie's husband who left his own researches to join his wife in hers, rather than vice versa.

Lise Meitner's active participation in the work that resulted in splitting the uranium atom had, unfortunately, to be terminated on the very verge of its success. She had long been collaborating with Otto Hahn when she was forced to flee from Nazi Germany, leaving Hahn and their more recent colleague, Fritz Strassmann, to complete the work. For its success in achieving atomic fission, Dr. Hahn received the Nobel Prize for 1944. To Lise Meitner came the unusual honor, shared with only two other women as yet, of election to membership in the Swedish Academy of Sciences in the country to which she had fled and where she was given lifelong opportunity to continue her scientific work.

Miss Meitner had known early that she wanted to study mathematics and physics. One of seven children in the family of a lawyer in Vienna, where she had been born, she attended the city's Academic High School and went from there to the University of Vienna. In her student days she read with unusual interest newspaper accounts that told of the discovery of radioactivity and of Marie

Curie's work in the isolation of radium. At this ancient university she had the good fortune, in 1902, to begin her studies in theoretical physics with Ludwig Boltzmann. It was truly good fortune for her, because in many universities in Europe at that time the theory that all things are composed of tiny invisible particles called atoms was by no means generally accepted by physicists. Professor Boltzmann, on the other hand, was one of its most zealous advocates. He explained the theory of the atom to Lise Meitner and her fellow students with enthusiasm. The recent discovery of radioactivity had, in his belief, supplied experimental proof that these tiny particles existed; nevertheless this theory was still being questioned or denied by many European and American scientists.

Like most physicists who accepted the atomic theory of that day, Professor Boltzmann did not then suspect that the discovery of radioactivity was soon going to revolutionize the accepted concept of the atom as nature's smallest particle—indivisible as well as invisible. The Greek, Democritus, who in the fifth century B.C. propounded the theory that all things are composed of invisible particles, all of them in constant motion, and all of them composed of the same matter but different in size, shape and weight, had named these tiny particles *atoms* because that is the Greek word for "indivisible." Nearly twenty-four centuries elapsed before science had been developed to the stage where men whose minds were receptive to the atomic theory had scientific equipment and accumulated knowledge to begin to investigate the validity of this theory in laboratories instead of, mainly, philosophizing about it theoretically as did the ancient

Greeks. Yet only a few years would have to pass after the discovery of radioactivity before men could attempt to prove experimentally the existence of still smaller particles within the atom. Lise Meitner, then, was ready to step into the field of atomic physics at the very beginning of the promising new period opened up by radioactivity; she had a strong training in mathematics, a capacity for work, and an imagination that was active in the realm of theoretical physics.

In America many years later, as a Visiting Professor at the Catholic University of America, she reminisced a little about the state and stage of atomic science in her younger days as she talked with a group of young finalists selected that year (1946) in our Annual Science Talent Search. In her youth, she told them, atoms were generally regarded as "solid unsplittable little lumps." Yet at least as far back as 1868 when the chemist Mendelejeff (a Russian) had arranged all known elements in his classic Periodic Table of Atomic Weights, certain scientists noticed rhythmic recurrences in the weight figures that suggested to them the possibility that atoms were composed of still smaller particles, even though others were still refusing to accept the existence of the atom itself. When she was approximately the age of the young group to whom she was talking, the discovery of radioactivity and radium (by two Frenchmen and a Polish woman) had spurred other scientists to the discovery of positive and negative charges of electricity, called protons and electrons, within the atom, and later of particles, called neutrons, that contained no charge at all.

Even before these elements within the atom had been

proved experimentally, she continued, theoretical scientists—men like Bohr (a Dane) and Einstein (a German)—had had an insight that enabled them to suggest that, if attacked in the right way, atoms might be broken into pieces. And so, she concluded, due to the work of an international group of scientists, the rising generation of physicists year by year was challenged to efforts in their laboratories all over Europe and America to achieve what theoretical physicists of their day believed possible.

Dr. Meitner's first step toward becoming one of the rising young physicists of her day was to go to Berlin in 1907, the year after she had received her Doctorate in Philosophy under Boltzmann in Vienna. She wanted to continue her studies in theoretical physics, and the best way to do that was to attend the lectures of Max Planck, one of the world's most notable physicists, at that time a professor at the University of Berlin. While attending the lectures, she wanted to do some experimental work, and found several opportunities for this. Because she had already done some work in radioactivity in Vienna, she decided to keep to that branch of research and work with a young chemist, Otto Hahn, who was (though he was completely unaware of it) starting on the pathway that would lead him to a Nobel Prize in Physics. A man of her own age, trained in organic chemistry, he had entered the field of radioactivity and was working at the Emil Fischer Institute in Berlin.

One block stood in her way. In those days the doors of the Fischer Institute were closed to women. Hahn proved eager enough to have her work with him to try to get around that prohibition. His own experimental work was done in the private laboratory of a higher-up at the institute, and he had no hope that Dr. Meitner could work there. However, he had been given an old carpenter shop on the first floor where radioactive measurements were to be carried out. He talked with Mr. Fischer and received permission for Dr. Meitner to work there, with the understanding that she would not enter the study rooms on the floor above. And so began a work relationship that Dr. Hahn himself has said ". . . was to have considerable influence in my scientific development. . . . What was originally intended [by Dr. Meitner] to be a short visit to Berlin resulted in a co-operation that lasted over thirty years." And a friendship, he added, that was to last much longer.

For a few years Dr. Meitner's co-operation was confined to what she could do in the carpenter shop without benefit of a laboratory. Some types of investigations could be undertaken immediately—measurement of rays emanating from radioactive materials, for example, and investigations of their physical properties. Finally Dr. Hahn succeeded in having another part of the institute's ground floor fitted up for chemical research; there Dr. Meitner's co-operation in practical work of a purely chemical nature was made possible. Here they worked, the organic chemist and the theoretical physicist, in those early years when the groundwork of the new science of the atom was being laid.

In 1912 the Kaiser Wilhelm Institute for Chemistry was opened as a part of the University of Berlin, and Hahn became a member (later chief) of its staff. Dr. Meitner became an assistant to Max Planck at the University's Institute for Theoretical Physics. Now the Hahn-Meitner co-operation in research could continue with greater facilities and an enlarged staff. Five years later this woman physicist to whom laboratory doors had been closed only a few years earlier was asked to organize and become head of a new Physical Department at the Kaiser Wilhelm Institute for Chemistry.

She was now in a favored position at a university and in a city where some of the world's best scientific minds were gathered. It gave her opportunity to keep abreast with work in nuclear physics wherever it was happening and bring it to her experimental researches with Hahn and other collaborators. The collaboration with Hahn was a fruitful one for both of them, Hahn bringing to it the background and knowledge of a gifted organic chemist and Meitner the background and knowledge of a gifted theoretical physicist and mathematician. Together they announced their discovery of the rare radioactive element protactinium in 1917.

Her own studies of beta rays continued in this period, and she was the first to maintain that, in the process of disintegration of radioactive materials, the emission of radiation follows rather than precedes the emission of the particles. She won for herself a distinguished reputation throughout the 1920's and received recognition in the award of the Liebnitz Medal of the Berlin Academy of Sciences in 1924 and the Lieber Prize of the Austrian Academy of Sciences in 1925. The following year she became Professor Extraordinary at the University of Berlin, a position she would be able to retain only until Hitler's anti-Semitic decrees made it no longer possible.

Because she was an Austrian subject, however, Nazi decrees did not at first affect her as drastically as they might have had she been a German citizen, or as they would be applicable to her after the Nazis entered Austria in 1938. Jewish scientists, and Aryans who opposed anti-Semitism openly after Hitler came to power in 1934, began to disappear from German universities. For a period, though, the change in government did not affect her work with Hahn—a work that took a turn neither of them had actually been anticipating when they turned to it in the middle 1930's.

To get a proper focus on this work which ended so dramatically with atomic fission—an achievement that might well have given atomic bombs to Hitler first had Hahn and Meitner so willed it—it is well to recognize that they had not set out to split the uranium atom so that Hitler or anybody else could make atomic bombs. They were investigating radioactive substances because they were scientists interested, at that moment, in the changes that could be made to occur in these substances by various scientists using various experimental methods in various laboratories. Meitner and Hahn had already worked with radium and thorium; they had thoroughly investigated radioactive protactinium which they had discovered years earlier. Dr. Meitner had written a book on Radioactivity and Nuclear Physics and was a world authority in that realm of physics. Like Hahn, she was an investigator with an unquenchable thirst to learn more and more. And they two were among the little group of laboratory scientists in the middle 1930's who were changing

one element into another element by devising techniques
that changed the atom's nucleus.

To show this change in three steps that do not attempt
a scientific explantion:

1. Every atom, as stated earlier, contains protons (positive electrical charges), electrons (negative charges), and
neutrons, with no charge at all. Its protons are congre-
gated in a hard mass in its nucleus, or core, which is only
a fraction of the size of the whole atom.*

2. The number of protons in an atom of any element
is identical with the number that element occupies in the
Table of Atomic Weights. Hydrogen, No. 1 in the Table,
has one proton. Oxygen, No. 8 in the Table, has eight
protons. Mercury, No. 80 in the Table, has eighty protons—and so on for each of the more than one hundred
elements.

3. In devising techniques for experimenting with
atoms in laboratories, scientists discovered it was possible
to remove a proton from the atom of some elements.
When they did this, the element they were working with
changed into the element next below it in the Table.
When they removed a proton from oxygen (No. 8), they
had nitrogen (No. 7). When they removed a proton from
lithium (No. 3), they had helium (No. 2). When they
removed a proton from mercury (No. 80), they had gold

---

* Dr. Meitner has described the size of an atom in this way: "By measuring
the radius of a soap bubble we can calculate the area of its spherical surface.
After bursting the bubble we can determine its weight and thus the thickness of the film. Such calculations show that soap bubbles are sometimes
less than one-millionth of a centimeter thick. Since the bubble must contain
at least one layer of soap molecules, these molecules must have diameters
smaller than one-millionth of a centimeter. And atoms composing the molecules must be even smaller."

(No. 79). In some cases (gold is one of them), the resulting element is unstable and soon changes of its own accord
into something else. In other cases the resulting element
is stable and retains its new form.

To return, now, to the Meitner-Hahn work: Changes
such as those described were frequently achieved before
it was known that the atom contained anything but protons and electrons. With the discovery of neutrons in
1932, new techniques were possible for experimental
work; down in Italy, in 1934, a group of scientists headed
by Enrico Fermi bombarded atoms of uranium (No. 92
in the Table and highest of all elements then known)
with neutrons and produced something that seemed un-
like any element then known. Fermi thought it must be
a new element higher than uranium in the Table of
Atomic Weights, possibly No. 93, which had not yet been
discovered in nature. Complete chemical analysis that
could make certain of this supposition was difficult in a
radioactive substance available only in the small quan-
tities in which their experiments had produced it, and
there was question about it in scientific minds. If, however, Fermi's supposition were correct, even the layman
can see that he would have been adding to rather than
subtracting from the number of protons in an atom's
nucleus—something new and exciting in the scientific
world of that day.

According to Dr. Hahn, when they heard in Berlin
about Fermi's experiments, "Lise Meitner and I decided
to repeat Fermi's work, being already familiar with the
chemical properties of protactinium." This was element
No. 91 on the Table, and the pair of scientists who had

discovered and investigated protactinium earlier had experience and knowledge that might well prove valuable in analyzing the substance Fermi had produced if it were near uranium and protactinium in the Table.

They began their work, and soon, says Dr. Meitner, "A whole new group of radioactive substances that could not be identical with any of the elements just below uranium in the Periodic Tables were discovered. Only one assumption was possible; they were higher." After a period Fritz Strassmann joined them in their work. "Further research," continues Dr. Meitner, "led to the discovery that we were dealing with an entirely new process." While they were puzzling over what was happening, the spring of 1938 arrived and Austria was occupied by the Nazis. At a crucial moment Lise Meitner's friends helped her out of Germany before it was too late, and she went, temporarily, to Copenhagen, where her sister's son, Otto Frisch, was working in the laboratory of Niels Bohr, sometimes spoken of as the father of the atom, who was then, as he would always remain, one of the most respected figures in the world of modern science.

In Berlin Hahn and Strassmann continued their work after Meitner left it. Soon (a few months) after her departure they completed chemical analyses that showed their "entirely new process" was producing barium. Hahn published this fact in a scientific journal early in January, 1939. It puzzled him because the results, he said, "were in opposition to all the phenomena observed up to the present in nuclear physics." Lise Meitner heard about it in Sweden, where she had found a place at the Physical Institute of the Academy of Sciences in Stockholm, and was not puzzled long. Knowing the Berlin work as she did, and comprehending Bohr's theory of the structure of the atom with the keenness of a gifted nuclear scientist, she grasped the meaning that had eluded Hahn. The appearance of barium indicated the great possibility that *the nucleus of the uranium atom* (No. 92) *had split.* If barium (No. 56 on the Table) had been produced, the gaseous element krypton (No. 36) had also been produced, she felt certain. She saw scientific reasons why this should happen.

She communicated her idea promptly to Frisch in Copenhagen, who communicated it to Bohr, who was just leaving for the United States for conferences with scientists here. Immediately, in a letter dated January 16, she and Frisch prepared a communication for the British scientific journal *Nature,* in which the result achieved by Hahn and Strassmann was described as a splitting of the uranium atom (she called it "atomic fission," and was the first to do so) and its scientific principles were elucidated to show that such fission was to be expected in the heaviest atomic nuclei. They calculated that almost 200 million electron volts of energy were released in the fission.

Niels Bohr landed in America the day that letter was written and communicated his news to scientist friends at Columbia and Princeton. Ten days later it was made public at a conference of American physicists in Washington. Probably no piece of news had ever caused greater excitement in this group. If fission of the uranium atom had actually been achieved with release of energy as Meitner and Frisch had calculated, the fact could be checked with apparatus (and brains!) existing in a number of American laboratories. Scientists rushed to telephones to get experimental work under way. Frisch was already at work on it in Bohr's laboratory in Copenhagen and succeeded in producing the proof first. American laboratories soon confirmed his results and the race was on—though for a long time without support of our Government—to see who would achieve a chain reaction in atomic fission first and thus be able to use atomic energy in bombs. It was in February, 1940—thirteen months after the announcement of atomic fission—that the first governmental funds were made available to scientists at Columbia University, some of whom would, in a new setting, eventually achieve a chain reaction. That grant was for $6000!

A few years and a world war later Dr. Meitner wrote: "It is an unfortunate accident that this discovery (atomic fission) came about in time of war." Since it did happen at that time, and since it happened in Germany, it was fortunate for America and her allies that Lise Meitner, a woman physicist, had the insight into nuclear physics which she possessed, and acted as she did. Scientists who remained in Germany were soon in a position where they were either unable or unwilling to communicate with scientists whose countries were at war with theirs. (Hahn succeeded in confining his work very largely to nonwar researches.) But all German scientists had not remained in Germany, nor all Italian scientists, in Italy. America and her allies reaped the results of anti-Semitic prejudices in those countries, in scientific achievements in which exiled European scientists played a great part. In fact, one must wonder what the world might have become if the madness of temporarily successful dictators had not betrayed them by the anti-Semitism that gave their foes the scientific talents that helped destroy the dictators.

Lise Meitner's residence in Stockholm became a permanent one and, necessarily, a none-too-happy one during the war years when Sweden maintained an uneasy neutrality and conditions surrounding friends in Germany were unthinkable. An acquaintance who saw her soon after her arrival in Stockholm described her as a "worried, tired woman with the tense expression all refugees had in common." Those days passed and better days came, even though the suffering endured for loved ones who did not escape the prison camps in Germany can never completely pass.

After a year's visit to America when the war was over, she returned to Sweden to take out citizenship papers there. As a member of the Atomic Research Staff of the University of Stockholm she has been able to continue her work well beyond the years when most scientists give it up. Honors came to her, not only from the Swedish nation, which made her the only living woman member of its Academy of Sciences, but from Germany and her native Austria as well. The City of Vienna's Prize in Sciences was awarded her in 1947, and the Max Planck Medal in 1949. Four American educational institutions— Syracuse, Rutgers, Smith and Adelphi—have given her honorary doctorates in science.

HELEN SAWYER HOGG

(1905–   )

• •

Toronto University astronomer whose work on variable
stars and globular star clusters has brought her the Annie
Jump Cannon Prize and eminence among scientists

NOT UNTIL she was a college junior did Helen Sawyer
have any idea that she would ever want to be an astronomer. She signed up for a course in astronomy that year
and the attraction of the stars, under the stimulation of
a teacher who was a devoted student of the skies, unexpectedly became strong enough to set the course for her
future. She transferred her major from chemistry to
astronomy when Mount Holyoke refused to permit a
double major, and has never regretted the change. The
stars have been her lifelong work. A wife, three times a
mother and a widow by the time she was forty-five, she
had already been honored with the Annie Jump Cannon
Prize in Astronomy. Since then she has gone on to increasing recognition among her peers.

As a child Helen Sawyer learned about the stars from her mother. Many a winter evening, in the yard of their home in Lowell, Massachusetts, Mrs. Sawyer pointed out Orion. At Lake Winnepesaukee, where they had a summer home, she showed her daughter other constellations and told her what she knew about the heavens. These were experiences no more stimulating than many others that came naturally to a child in the home of a well-to-do New England banker—an only child after the marriage of her beloved sister when Helen was only five or six. Quite as interesting as the stars were her mother's collection of rocks, the flowers she pressed, the New England poets whose nature poems she often quoted. Helen herself made a collection of rare ferns and hybrids during several summer vacations spent at a cousin's farm in Vermont.

Of equal pleasure were the Sunday afternoon walks with her father along the Merrimac River by the Pawtucket Falls or, after he had purchased one of Lowell's early automobiles, the drives in which they sometimes explored old cemeteries to locate graves of early American ancestors. Seeing the monument at Groton commemorating the slaughter of William and Deliverance Longley with five of their eight children was an unforgettable experience to a small girl who traced her ancestry back to one of the three children who escaped that massacre.

Her father lived only until she was twelve. After his death, as before it, Helen attended the public schools of Lowell. Living in her home for many years was a distant relative, Miss Leonora Battles, who became one of the city's outstanding grade school teachers. "Auntie" Battles was unquestionably an influence in Helen's educational development, added to that of her parents. Respect for education and helpful attitudes toward it surrounded this child all her young life. Summers at the lake continued to be happy, carefree vacation months each year. School days were happy days, too, even though not so carefree. Helen liked her studies—all of them—and stood in the top half-dozen of her class of several hundred at Lowell High in the spring of 1921, at her graduation several months before her sixteenth birthday.

She was now prepared for college, money for it was available, and Mount Holyoke was her choice. But she was young. Possibly it would be better not to leave home for another year. She went back to Lowell High for a fifth year's work, and when she left for college the following September, "Mount Holyoke seemed halfway around the world to me." Little could she have anticipated that thirty-six years later she would board a plane for a visit to Russia on invitation from the Soviet Government, scarcely more impressed by the distances she would travel than she had been by the distance that lay that day between Lowell and South Hadley, Massachusetts.

Nor could she have anticipated, that September day in 1922, that her concept of distance would have been expanded to the extent that in only a few years she would be helping to measure stellar distances in millions of light-year units. Had anyone suggested that in the short space of four years she would become an assistant to Dr. Harlow Shapley, who had recently been appointed Director of the Harvard Observatory, it would have seemed a fantastic impossibility. Astronomy was far from her mind as she set out for college. She took chemistry in her freshman year, a subject to which she had not been introduced in five years of high-school work, chose it as her major at the end of that year and was quite content about it. Content, that is, until her orbit crossed the orbit of Dr. Anne Sewell Young. And life has never been the same for Helen Sawyer since that happened to her.

As is suggested elsewhere in this book, Mount Holyoke had an excellent chemistry department. It also had a strong astronomy department, headed by the niece of Dr. Charles Augustus Young, Princeton University's distinguished professor of astronomy for more than twenty-five years and a pioneer in the study of the spectrum of the sun's corona. Anne Sewell Young, Director of the John Payson Williston Observatory at Mount Holyoke when Helen Sawyer went to college, had been cut over the same pattern as her uncle. The stars were her life, and so electric were their effects upon her, she was likely to electrify her students in turn if they brought with them innate capacities for scientific study of the heavens.

Helen Sawyer was still in her teens when, signing up as a junior for her first course in astronomy in complete innocence of what it was going to do to her, her pathway coalesced for a period with Dr. Young's. She felt the tingle of it, not only in the observatory, where an excellent telescope gave her a more intimate view of Orion than she had had from the yard of her home in Lowell, but in the classroom that fall, where Dr. Young was an inspiring teacher.

A few weeks after Christmas vacation that year the sun very obligingly came due for a total eclipse. This is an event of first-rate importance to astronomers everywhere, sending some of them halfway round the world in order to get the best possible view of it. That eclipse of 1925, however, was an event whose importance at Mount Holyoke was not to be limited to students of astronomy, even though South Hadley itself was not in the pathway of totality. Central Connecticut, a mere hundred miles or so to the south, lay in that pathway, and Dr. Young electrified college authorities into arranging for a special train, to be boarded before dawn, to carry the entire student body to central Connecticut. The train stopped that cold January morning in the midst of a bare field where, standing knee-deep in snow, teeth chattering, but without even the twig of a tree branch to mar the view, Mount Holyoke students and braver members of its faculty observed one of the most magnificent spectacles it is man's privilege to witness—a total eclipse of the sun on a clear day.

That generation of Mount Holyoke women still enjoy not only the memory of a total eclipse but the memory that Harvard undergraduates en masse missed the spectacle because, for various reasons (it was explained later) "it was not feasible" for them to be at the right spot at the right moment. They also enjoy remembering that no one died of pneumonia as a resut of the unfeasible having been made feasible for them, though, "I don't believe I ever knew what it meant to be cold before that morning," Dr. Hogg admits.

During her senior year another event of high importance in her life occurred. Dr. Annie Jump Cannon visited Mount Holyoke and became acquainted with the work of some of its young astronomy students. Dr. Cannon was the Harvard astronomer who classified nearly 400,000 stars and whose contributions were later described by Dr. Shapley as constituting "a structure that will probably never be duplicated in kind or extent by a single individual." The result of her visit was that it was arranged for Miss Sawyer to have the Edward C. Pickering Scholarship at Radcliffe the next year and begin work that could eventually lead to a Ph.D. in astronomy.

Before her graduation, with membership in Phi Beta Kappa, in 1926, Helen Sawyer had become interested in the clusters of stars belonging to our Milky Way System, known as globular star clusters. As it happened, this was one of Dr. Harlow Shapley's special interests, too. So when Miss Sawyer picked up her scholarship at Radcliffe that fall, it became her privilege to work with the Harvard Observatory's director. (Postgraduate work in astronomy at Radcliffe and Harvard were identical, though doctorates were given by each institution in its own name.) Results of some of that first year's work appeared in a 1927 issue of the *Bulletin* of the Harvard College Observatory, whose first paper, "Photographic Magnitudes of Ninety-Five Globular Clusters," is signed by Helen Sawyer and Harlow Shapley, and in that order!

Interestingly enough, the last paper in that same issue is signed by a Harvard graduate student, Frank S. Hogg, a young Canadian who had graduated the previous spring from the University of Toronto. Mr. Hogg's special field was stellar spectrophotometry, and to this young Canadian was to come the distinction of receiving, in 1929, the first Ph.D. in astronomy ever granted by Harvard. Naturally enough Helen Sawyer and Frank Hogg met. They soon found they had many interests in common— personal as well as professional ones.

Though each of them received a Master's degree in 1928, it was going to take Miss Sawyer two years longer to attain her doctorate from Radcliffe than it took Frank Hogg at Harvard. It took neither of them overlong to fall in love with each other, but marriage had to wait a while. Miss Sawyer had fellowships of one kind or another for the whole of her work at Radcliffe and left her studies there for several months one year to meet an emergency at Smith College by serving as an instructor there. When he had his Ph.D., Frank Hogg went off on a year's traveling fellowship to Cambridge, England, while Miss Sawyer continued her work at Cambridge in the U.S.A., where she had begun to specialize in variable stars in globular clusters and was in the midst of some brilliant work in them. They married when Dr. Hogg returned to accept a position at Amherst College for a year, during which Mrs. Hogg taught astronomy at Mount Holyoke while completing the work that gave her a rather hard-earned doctorate from Radcliffe.

So fruitful had her investigations of the stars been before her marriage, the name Sawyer was by that time well established in the literature of variable stars and globular clusters. For that reason Dr. Helen Sawyer Hogg's scientific work in her specialized field is always recorded under her maiden name, although in other professional life, as in social life, she uses her married name. Hers is a case where adoption of the English custom of a hyphenated Sawyer-Hogg would have had its advantages.

In the fall of 1931 the two Dr. Hoggs were off to British Columbia, where Frank Hogg had been appointed to the staff of the Dominion Astrophysical Observatory in Victoria. No paid position was available for his wife, but to her was granted the privilege, for a few nights each year, of using the observatory's 72-inch reflecting telescope, the second biggest reflector in the world at that time. An eventful three years lay ahead, years in which Dr. Helen Hogg's "salary" would average around $250 per year through research grants the observatory's Director, Dr. J. S. Plaskett, was able to help her secure. They were years, too, in which young Sally's arrival complicated her mother's life somewhat. Children, however, were welcome complications for these two, whose devotion to the mysteries of the heavens did nothing to minimize their need for a full life that included home and community responsibilities. Two sons followed Sally in due time, and they were three bulwarks for their mother when Frank Hogg's brilliant life was cut short at forty-six, after twenty years of marriage.

Though the 72-inch reflector, in use since 1918, had never before been used for a research program of direct photography, it was well planned and adapted for this use. With co-operation from her husband and others at the observatory, Dr. Hogg undertook, that fall of 1931, her first program "on her own" in the field of her choice by taking pictures of eight selected globular star clusters visible in Victoria's night skies. Some of these clusters were known to contain variable stars, others had never been diligently searched.

To explain a little, before going farther, about globular clusters and why astronomers are interested in them: Globular clusters are symmetrical aggregations of hundreds of thousands of stars, held together in a cluster by gravitation. They belong to our Milky Way system of some 100,000 million stars. Individual clusters, of which, more than one hundred are known today, range from a few thousand stars to a hundred thousand or more.

Variable stars in globular clusters are those that grow brighter and dimmer at regular intervals. They are of particular importance because they are used in computing stellar distances. Astronomers measure distances between earth and other objects in space by a mathematical process based on the degree of light (called magnitude) a variable radiates at its brightest and dimmest moments, and the period of time elapsing between the two extremes. So not only the discovery of variables but the far more difficult measurement of their magnitude and time periods is of the utmost importance in astronomy.

The first practical need, then, of the astronomer making the type of study Dr. Hogg was about to undertake is to be able to take successful, and successive, photographs of the heavens, registering light. After that comes competence in study of the plates and in their interpretation, with capacity for deriving sound conclusions based upon the new plates, often in conjunction with study of other plates that may already exist of the same cluster. Facility with higher mathematics is a requisite for some of this.

In the three years the Hoggs spent at the Dominion

Observatory Dr. Hogg took (with her husband's and other assistance) some 350 to 400 direct photographs of globular clusters. In the cluster known as Messier 2 she found six new variables. Using her 107 new plates of this cluster with 28 plates that had been taken at the Mt. Wilson Observatory earlier, she determined, and published, the magnitudes and time periods of all the 17 then known variables in this cluster. In five of the other clusters she had selected for study she found 132 new variables, an increase of 10 per cent of the variables previously known in these clusters. Actually, in four of these clusters no variables at all had been known earlier.

Unquestionably this first research program yielded results of value to astronomers. To the layman who knows little about an astronomer's techniques, interest is increased if he is able to visualize something of how this kind of work is done. So picture Dr. Hogg sitting on a movable platform up at the top of the dome, her eye, for the full period of the exposure of each plate, steadily pressed against the eyepiece of the camera attached to the end of the telescope, her fingers slowly manipulating a delicate mechanism by which she keeps the cluster in steady focus as her eye follows its motion in space.

Exposure times for that set of photographs ranged from one or two minutes to twenty-five to thirty minutes. Later she would take photographs requiring an hour's exposure—sixty minutes of keeping her eye glued to the eyepiece. "Of course, I did have to wink," she explains almost apologetically.

This type of photography has to be done between sunset and sunrise during the limited number of months in the year when the stars are in their best position for it and the nights clear enough for good results. As it happened, young Sally's feeding problems had to be coped with one summer. She was carried by her parents to the observatory in a comfortably fitted clothes basket in which she slept healthfully in the outdoors, under her father's eye, on the floor of the dome where he regulated the mechanism by which the telescope was set and the dome revolved. At intervals between pictures her mother would push the electric button that lowered her platform to the floor, give her child nourishment and other attentions. Then Sally would be returned to her basket and her mother to the top of the dome. All in all it was a creative period in more than astronomy that summer, punctuated once by a visit from the Astronomer Royal, who uttered a startled, "What's that!" as he and the observatory Director were ascending the steps to the floor of the dome one starlit night at a moment when Sally happened to give a little whimper.

"Oh, that's the Hoggs' baby," its parents heard Dr. Plaskett explain to his distinguished guest.

When the new four-domed David Dunlap Observatory at the University of Toronto was nearing completion, Dr. Frank Hogg was called to the staff of this university's department of astronomy. His wife became an assistant—her first salaried job since receiving her Ph.D. —at the observatory, where a 74-inch reflector would be an admirable tool for continuing her researches in a field in which the name Sawyer was becoming increasingly well known, as was her husband's for his work in spectroscopy. Frank Hogg's advancement at Toronto was rapid. He was a brilliant astronomer whose early death from a heart condition was truly a tragedy. At the age of forty-one he became Director of the observatory; at forty-six he was dead. But seventeen years of life as a co-operative domestic and professional venture lay ahead of these two when they came east to the university that has been Helen Sawyer Hogg's professional center ever since. By the fall of 1937 their two sons had been born, and the next year Dr. Helen Hogg advanced to the position of Research Associate at the observatory. This was the beginning of her ascent to a full professorship on the university faculty in 1957, an honor still rare for a woman scientist at that university, as at many others.

Up to and for five years after her work at the David Dunlap Observatory began, Helen Sawyer's studies of globular star clusters had been done with the use of telescopes situated in the northern part of the United States or southern Canada. Since some globular clusters are photographed best in southern skies, she wanted photographs she did not yet have. A grant from the National Academy of Sciences in 1939, and promise of co-operation from the University of Arizona and the director of its observatory would now make this possible, through use of its 36-inch Steward reflector.

Just before beginning this new series of photographs, she brought to completion her *Catalogue of 1116 Variable Stars in Globular Star Clusters,* a contribution greatly welcomed by astronomers. Published in 1939, the value of this exhaustive piece of research was in no way lessened because work on it had lent itself well to the period in her life when her two small sons needed much personal attention from their mother. Catalogues of stars are of great importance in astronomy. Several summaries (including one by Dr. Shapley) of variable stars in globular clusters had appeared by the early 1930's, but no complete catalogue of them had ever been published until Dr. Hogg's. It enabled any worker interested in variables to know exactly what had been done, up to that time, on all known variables in globular clusters, either for clusters as a whole or for any individual cluster. (In 1939 time periods had been determined on only 656 of the variables.) Study of that catalogue reveals that more than half of its recorded variables had been discovered before Helen Sawyer had been born, the first one way back in 1860. Of the 500 to 600 discovered since her birth, she herself had discovered 142.

Southern skies as seen through the Steward reflector gave a new experience to Dr. Hogg when she went down to the University of Arizona in the summer of 1939 to begin work on the 279 direct photographs she made there. By this time she knew very well how much work her increasing number of photographic plates was amassing for her. Adding to man's knowledge of the universe by examination and study of photographic plates by any and all means possible—superposition of a positive and a negative, or examination by a blink microscope, to mention two of the methods she was using—is a meticulous, time-consuming type of work, demanding close attention. Literally hundreds of stars may be searched for the discovery of one variable. After that comes the work of measuring its brightness, dimness, and time interval. And often, just as an astronomer gets on the trail of the secret of the star's time interval, the moonlight becomes too bright to permit work on such faint objects and continuity of the work is broken.

Notwithstanding the sheer labor they necessitated, the variable stars were a field to which Helen Sawyer was dedicated, one to which she devoted much time all through the 1940's as she continued her lecturing and teaching at the university, took new pictures with its observatory's telescope, and accepted the many human responsibilities and pleasures that concerned her home and the community in which she and her husband were taking their share of citizenly duties. One of these years she managed to answer a call from Mount Holyoke to serve as acting head of its astronomy department while its observatory's director witnessed an eclipse in South America. It was hard work to carry regular responsibilities at Mount Holyoke and get back to Toronto as often as possible. But, "There was a genuine shortage of people prepared to take over Dr. Farnsworth's work, and she might not have been able to see that eclipse if I had not helped out," Dr. Hogg comments. Eclipses are of immense importance to astronomers, and one of them who had stood knee-deep in snow to see an eclipse was not likely to forget it.

One by one papers over Helen Sawyer's name appeared in Canadian, American and, occasionally, foreign scientific journals. Usually they reported data on new variables of her own discovery or magnitudes she had determined on variables whose data had not previously been completed. Her *Bibliography of Individual Globular Clusters* appeared in 1947, giving astronomers information on where they could find all literature, to date, in this field. Occasionally she was able to report correction of errors made by astronomers in computing time periods. When, in 1950, she became the recipient of the Annie Jump Cannon Prize for her outstanding contributions to astronomy, chiefly for her studies of the globular clusters, she was described as having "attained the leading position in this difficult field." Four years earlier her work had won her election as a Fellow of the Royal Society of Canada, the only woman ever so honored in the field of physical science.

Always more work seemed to lie ahead than had already been done. New globular clusters were found as telescopes became more powerful in various parts of the globe. But that was not the only type of discovery being made. Observational evidence began to accumulate showing that new stars were being created! The long accepted theory that the stars had all been formed at the same time was discarded. The universe was seen to be in the process of creation.

This was a radical change in basic astronomical thinking, and Helen Sawyer's thought moved with it. She had no tendency to imitate the Italian nobleman who refused to look through Galileo's telescope for fear he would believe what he saw there. Hers was the faith of the astronomer who had said, "The undevout astronomer is mad." And all of it was necessary that New Year's morning of 1951 when, with the three children at home and all of them waiting for their father to come down to breakfast, she went up to waken him and found him dead.

Never had the years been busier than she made them after that. The university advanced her rank and salary. Requests for her to pick up her husband's activities outside the university were answered affirmatively whenever possible. The "Out of Old Books" column she had been writing for the *Journal of the Royal Astronomical Society of Canada* continued without a break as she assumed new writing responsibilities that had been her husband's. Sally went back to college, the boys finished high school and began their college education, one in astronomy and the other in chemistry. A new assistant took Frank Hogg's place on the floor of the dome when Helen Sawyer took photographs of the stars. Her plates mounted in numbers and so did the work on them. In 1955, when she published her *Second Catalogue of Variable Stars in Globular Clusters*, it contained 329 new ones, discovered since the first *Catalogue* had been published. Of the 329, 30 per cent of them—99 new variables—had been discovered by Helen Sawyer.

Recognition has come to her other than the high academic tribute given her by her Toronto University in electing her to a full professorship in 1957. The National Science Foundation asked her to direct its program for astronomy in 1955, the only woman who has ever held that position. The Royal Astronomical Society of Canada elected her to its Presidency in 1957. Mount Holyoke awarded her an honorary doctorate in science in 1958. As a delegate and member of the International Astronomical Union, and president of its subcommission on variable stars in globular clusters, she enjoyed the hospitality of the Soviet Academy of Sciences in Moscow in August, 1958, for two weeks of meetings and official tours.

With it all Helen Hogg finds time for her writing, including her weekly *"With the Stars"* column in the Toronto *Daily Star.* She finds time to get acquainted with the grandchildren who began to appear when she reached fifty, and for the expert knitting into which she tacks very professional labels stating "From the Knitting Needle of Helen Hogg." She is a woman of science who has admirably combined the art of homemaking and of friendship with high caliber professional work outside the home. Hers has been a life full of responsibilities that have brought her a human maturity that does not accrue merely through advancing years and intellectual activity but arrives only when body, mind, and heart—or spirit—move along in active unison with each other.

ELIZABETH SHULL RUSSELL

(1913–   )

●●

Zoologist-geneticist whose studies with house mice are
helping to reveal the physiological processes used by
genes in producing their effects

Genetics is the scientific study of heredity, and a close
look at Elizabeth Shull's family makes a person wonder
how much heredity had to do with making her a geneticist. Five of the six farm-boy brothers in her father's
family, including her geneticist father, became biological
scientists. Her mother (née Buckley) had an A.M. in
zoology and taught this subject for several years before
she married Dr. Shull. Of their two children, Elizabeth
became a zoologist who turned, like her father, toward
genetics, while her brother became a physicist, like her
mother's brother Oliver. With both Buckleys and Shulls
it seems a clear case of scientific talent "running in the
family."

Yet the geneticist knows that environment as well as

heredity plays a part in determining what we become. In Elizabeth Shull's case early environment tended, possibly, to turn her more to botany than to zoology—the two main divisions of biology between which a geneticist has usually made his earlier choice. As a schoolgirl of ten or eleven with an interest in both plants and animals, she spent absorbed hours of a summer vacation making a survey of all flowering plants in a woodland lot near her home, examining each plant and identifying its species. Under her mother's expert instruction each plant was then pressed and mounted. When she finished, she had an herbarium good enough to make a very creditable exhibit a few years later when she was a high school junior taking her first course in biology.

Except for being a year or two younger than most students in her grade, Elizabeth's high-school life was similar to that of many other girls in high-standard American high schools. In Ann Arbor, where she had been born and where her father was a professor of zoology at the University of Michigan, the university had a high school which faculty children usually attended. Here she was fortunate to have instruction from a man who taught students a method of learning as well as subject matter. In his biology classes Professor Francis D. Curtis taught the scientific approach to a subject. A hypothesis would be stated and each student, on the basis of his knowledge pertaining to factors included in the hypothesis, would guess what would happen. Then the problem would be worked out step by step so that each student could see how to prove—or disprove—a hypothesis. For example: What makes bread mold? On the basis of his experience one student might suggest that dampness was a necessary factor. Another might think temperature changes were necessary and a third that exposure to light was a factor. Still another might suggest that mold organisms from outside itself had to be present before bread became moldy. All these suggestions became a series of hypotheses to be proved or disproved, and experimental tests began.

Slices of bread as identical as possible were used. Some were kept dry and exposed to light or lack of it; some were dampened and exposed to light or lack of it. Other slices, both dry and dampened, were exposed to a piece of moldy bread, then to light or lack of it, while others of identical dryness or dampness, light or lack of it, were kept in sterile circumstances—and so on. In the end the students learned experimentally exactly what did and did not happen—and always with plenty of questions which Professor Curtis showed them how to find answers for themselves, if possible.

Thus, in a class in biology when she was in her early teens, Elizabeth Shull learned one of the basic techniques of the scientific method—that is, state a hypothesis, then prove it right or wrong. This was the method Lise Meitner illustrated so strikingly when she stated, on the basis of her knowledge of nuclear physics, what she believed had happened in Otto Hahn's laboratory after she had left it to flee from Germany (see page 28). Dr. Meitner made her brilliant hypothesis that the atom had been split and furnished scientific reasoning in support of her thesis. Proof came quickly in a number of laboratories where practical tests could be made. This method, which Professor Curtis's pupils were taught, is very different from the right-or-wrong, true-or-false guessing games that have become a part of our educational system, in which students guess without learning the processes that develop the reasoning faculty and often have a fifty-fifty chance of being right no matter how little they know about the subject.

Barely sixteen when she was ready for college, Elizabeth Shull had made her decision to become a biology teacher in secondary schools. Vacations at summer camps where nature study had been part of the program had kept her interest in both plants and animals alive and growing. One event had occurred in high school that may, she thinks, have contributed to increasing her interest in zoology. For one of her biology projects under Professor Curtis she gathered scum from the top of a stagnant pond to make a culture in which she could study types of life in it. Pond scum, she knew, contained both plant and animal organisms. She fed her culture boiled rice and rice water for a month until it was rich in Paramecia—a kind of single-cell organism that reproduces itself by dividing into two parts. Hour after hour she watched these tiny organisms under her microscope, till finally came the thrill of *seeing* one of them divide. What had been one living animal cell became two living animal cells. It was a rewarding experience for a schoolgirl. She never forgot it.

Whether or not this experience was of much influence, she chose zoology and general science as her majors at the University of Michigan, with a minor in chemistry and mathematics. As had been true in high school, she

liked and made good marks in all her studies. She took
a couple of courses in botany and, during two summer
vacations, worked as a counselor in a camp where she
taught nature study. Two other summers at the University's Biological Station revealed how fascinating work
with animals could be, too. They did so many more
things than plants, had so much greater diversity. Possibly the fact that she always liked animals as animals
made her a little averse to wanting to make use of them
for laboratory study in a lifework. She is a compassionate
human being who might understandably have met this
type of unconscious block that kept her from recognizing
what her greatest interest would be.

At any rate Miss Shull still planned to teach biology
when she was graduated from the University of Michigan
as a member of Phi Beta Kappa and with special distinction in zoology in 1933. At her father's suggestion she
applied for a scholarship paying room and board at
Columbia for a year's postgraduate work in zoology,
and got it. In the course of that year something
happened that often happens earlier in a science student's
life—the "something" that makes a young person know
the field in which he wants to work more than in any
other. At Columbia Miss Shull had her first work in
theoretical genetics. She had had a course in heredity at
Michigan in which she studied the kinds of things genes
can do in transmitting hereditary characteristics, and had
found this subject interesting but not overpowering. In
her Columbia course attention was focused not on the
transmission of hereditary units from generation to generation but on *the physiological processes by which genes*

produce their effects in the lifetime of a single animal. Let her describe what happened to her in her own words: "I came across some papers by Sewall Wright of the University of Chicago telling about work he had done in trying to trace the physiological processes used by certain genes in producing hereditarily-determined characteristics. This gripped my interest as nothing had ever quite gripped it before. Almost without my knowing it, something gelled in me. By the time I had my M.A. that following spring, I knew I wanted to be a geneticist, and headed for Chicago and Dr. Wright."

Three years followed in which she studied and served as an assistant in Dr. Wright's department at the University of Chicago—a "crucially important experience," she calls it, and one that gave direction to her life. Dr. Wright had been studying the pigmentation of guinea pigs, trying to trace processes by which genes produced the various colors in his animals' coats. All these colors—black, brown, deep tawny red, creamy yellow, piebald patterns on a white background, and the white of the albino animals—were produced under the influence of certain genes, and all genes were derived from parents. What he was trying to discover was how—that is, by what physiological processes—genes responsible for pigmentation did their colorful work.

By the time Elizabeth Shull arrived there to take up her work it was known that genes caused a source of color to be deposited locally, for guinea pigs shed constantly and grow new hair, and the color markings remain the same throughout life. Also, it was known that if skin is exchanged between black and white regions of a spotted guinea pig, the skin from the black region continues to produce black hairs and the skin from the white region produces white hairs, even though each bit of transplanted skin is surrounded by skin producing the opposite color. All this was known to happen, but the processes by which it happened were still largely a mystery, and it was a mystery that was soon fascinating Elizabeth Shull.

When the time came for her decision on a project and thesis for her Doctor's degree, she chose a problem in pigmentation. Under Dr. Wright's guidance she embarked upon a study, financed in part by a grant from the Rockefeller Foundation, in which she would make actual measurements of the effects of certain genes on the color of guinea pig coats. Understanding of this study is beyond the layman, but it included the chemical separation, from the hair, of melanin (the substance that produces color), weighing it, and comparing the amounts present in sepia, pale sepia, red, and yellow guinea pig hair of many different color intensities, thereby determining the effects of many different genes interacting with each other in the local process of pigmentation. To read the dissertation she presented on the results of this study is to draw the conclusion that she earned the Ph.D. she received in 1937.

While this lengthy study was in process, Elizabeth Shull had married a fellow zoologist-geneticist student. Work for his doctorate was completed a few months before hers, and he had gone to Bar Harbor, Maine, to become a research scientist at the Roscoe B. Jackson Memorial Laboratory there. This was a comparatively young institution, financially able at that time to employ a very limited number of scientists. It was, as it is today, dedicated to study of the role of heredity in mammalian behavior and disease. Its budget was too limited to offer a salary to a second Dr. Russell, but when she had attained her Ph.D. Elizabeth Shull Russell was given use of its facilities to work as an independent investigator in the same laboratory that was providing her husband with a modest salary that would support their home.

One type of research in which the Jackson Laboratory was particularly interested was the hereditary aspects of susceptibility to tumors. Shortly after Elizabeth Russell's arrival there she received an Elizabeth Pemberton Nourse Fellowship from the American Association of University Women with which to study the physiological genetics of tumor production in the fruit fly, an insect from whose study so much of man's knowledge of the behavior of genes has come. She chose, quite naturally, to study the type of tumor designated as "melanotic" because it results from abnormal deposits of melanin.

On the $1250 grant she received from the fellowship she was able to prove and disprove certain hypotheses made in respect to the malignant or nonmalignant nature of these tumors, and to determine location of some of the genes influencing their appearance in the fruit fly. By the time these studies were completed and ready for publication, she had become interested in the coat color of the mouse and in other characteristics of the various inbred strains of mice that were being bred at the Jackson Laboratory for use in research. But a more immediate job was facing her—the bearing and rearing of a family of her own. Three sons and a daughter were born between 1940-46, and in that humanly productive period Elizabeth Russell had very little time to spend in a laboratory. She retained her status as an independent investigator, nevertheless, did a little scientific work, and after the birth of her fourth and last child, and with the aid of a Finney-Howell Research Fellowship carrying a grant of $2500, completed in 1947 an intensive study of the pigment granules of thirty-six different mutant types of mice. In this study she was able to obtain a rather precise picture of the effects of certain genes on pigmentation processes.

Then came two devastating blows in rapid succession—a domestic crisis that left her with four small children to care for and a forest fire ranging over Mt. Desert that completely obliterated the Roscoe B. Jackson Memorial Laboratory practically at the moment when she received her appointment as a salaried research associate on its staff. All that was left of its equipment or work in progress was whatever records staff members happened to have at home on that catastrophic day in October, 1947.

The most serious laboratory loss was its animals. Not a single mouse survived: 90,000 of them perished—almost all from strains of standardized mice with carefully kept pedigrees. This was a serious blow to hundreds of other institutions where these animals were being used in medical research because of the many similarities between mice and human beings. Mice are mammals who suckle their young, as do human beings. They are vertebrates whose bony structures are comparable to those of human beings; they are warm-blooded with the same type of red blood cells human beings have; their endocrine systems perform the same functions as do human endocrine systems. All these similarities make them invaluable research animals for scientists.

Moreover, these little animals are susceptible to many of the same diseases to which human beings are susceptible. They pass susceptibility (or strong resistance) to these diseases along to their children and children's children, as do human beings. One of the valuable contributions the Jackson Laboratory had been making to science was the development of inbred strains of house mice in which every mouse would, with virtual certainty, become a victim of cancer, or of anemia, extreme obesity, or some other disease it had been inbred to develop. In all its strains each mouse was as like its hundreds of brothers and sisters as identical twins are alike. Scientists in many parts of the world were depending on the Jackson Laboratory to provide "identical twins" of earlier mice, as needed, to continue researches, knowing the new animals would react exactly as had those with which a research had begun. And suddenly, in the course of a few hours, every carefully bred, pedigreed, properly labeled mouse in the colony from which these experimental animals were being obtained was gone. The loss was felt literally all over the world.

To Elizabeth Russell was delegated responsibility for rebuilding this vital part of the Jackson Laboratory work, even before construction of the new laboratory was underway. From different parts of the world research centers voluntarily began to ship pedigreed mice with their proper labels back to Bar Harbor so that the Jackson Laboratory could be built up again. Fortunately, mice breed early and rapidly—only nineteen days from conception to birth. Females often have eight litters by the time they are a year old. But the inbred strains had to be rebuilt from small beginnings because comparatively few were available, and it was more than a year before many of them could be spared for research purposes. By 1950, however, the inbred strains were available in greater numbers than before the fire.

Some idea of the extent of this aspect of Dr. Russell's work (which she thinks of as service to science in general and quite apart from her own scientific work) may be gained by quoting a few statistics that show what was being accomplished ten years after the fire: in 1957 3000 mice were being born at the Jackson Laboratory daily—the heredity of each mouse was known and recorded in detail; 67 different strains existed, 28 of them inbred strains; animals in each strain were standardized and uniform; 7500 mice were leaving the laboratory each week—some 400,000 in a year. Many of them went by air to 600 laboratories in 22 countries, ranging from Kenya in Africa to Korea, and from southern Argentina to northern Europe. The mouse population at the Bar Harbor laboratory was about a million, and plans were underway for doubling that production, so great was the need and demand for the animals.

But all that was apart from Dr. Russell's work as a physiological geneticist as she planned and, as soon as space in the new building was available, began new researches that attempt to reveal the physiological processes by which genes achieve whatever effects they produce. New pigmentation studies were made, some of them with a younger physiological geneticist, Dr. Willys K. Silvers, in which skin from embryo mice destined to produce hair of one color was transplanted to newborn mice of another hair color. New knowledge of the action of genes came to light when it was clearly shown that certain "triggering mechanisms" producing color acted in the hair follicle and not in the pigment-producing cell.

Because certain genes that affect coat pigmentation also have severe effects on blood formation and on germ-cell multiplication, Dr. Russell's attention turned quite naturally to hereditary anemias and to sterility in mice. Investigations made in collaboration with Dr. Kurt Altman, in which blood-forming tissue from normal mice was transplanted to mice that had been bred to develop anemia, gave results indicating that the effects of anemia-producing genes is directly in the blood forming cells rather than imposed by the genes in cells in other parts of the body. Still another study—this one in collaboration with an embryologist, Dr. Beatrice Mintz—seems to have settled a problem about sterility about which scientists have argued for nearly a century. It is a problem too scientific to be described clearly here, but it has to do with the place of origin and travel route of the germ cells, which multiply rapidly in the early life of normal embryos but do not increase in numbers in defective embryos.

To date, however, the aspect of Dr. Russell's work that holds greatest interest for the layman lies in the field of muscular dystrophy. The story of her discovery of Funnyfoot, the first experimental animal ever known to be afflicted with hereditary muscular dystrophy strongly resembling the type that afflicts human beings, ties in with another feature of the Jackson Laboratory work in which she was greatly interested—its summer educational program. Each summer the laboratory accepts two groups of apprentices—one of college students and the other of pre-college students—for training in science and its techniques. Since Dr. Russell enjoys teaching, she likes to work with these summer students.

While this program was in progress in 1951, she was looking at a breeding cage with a litter of young mice and noticed one of them dragging its foot—"Funnyfoot," she called it quite naturally. Geneticists are constantly on the lookout for animals that differ from their mates, but when they find a variant animal, they know its differences are quite possibly due to some environmental disturbance (to poor nutrition or mechanical damage which produces what they call "box-top deviants," or to a disease organism). Only rarely does a gene "slip a cog" and miscopy itself, apparently spontaneously, to produce a new type—or mutant—which transmits this difference hereditarily to its offspring. Geneticists do not know *why* or *how* this happens, but they know the mutant is the result of a change in one gene pair only, while animals that are bred to become certain victims of (or very susceptible to) some disease are produced through combinations of genes that give rise to the hereditary tendency. When a mutant occurs, they want to find out all they can about the nature of the mutation and its effects.

When Funnyfoot appeared that summer, Dr. Russell set one of her apprentices, Ann Michelson of Smith College, to the task of tracing the cause of its affliction— an affliction which soon began to appear in occasional other baby mice born in the same strain. Soon they determined that the funnyfoot abnormality did indeed have a hereditary basis. Under Dr. Russell's guidance Miss Michelson tested the mouse first for nervous disorders and found none. With help from other experts in the laboratory as needed, she proceeded with neuroanatomical and pathological tests, concluding her studies during her senior year at Smith. The conclusion reached was that Funnyfoot was the victim of a hereditary muscle disease similar to the dystrophies which afflict and cripple human beings.

As soon as the similarity of Funnyfoot's affliction to human muscular dystrophy was established, scientists investigating this disease wanted afflicted mice and their normal littermates for research studies. But Funnyfoot, unfortunately for science, was in exceeding short supply. Only one or two were born to occasional litters. Not only did those that were born die young (in one to six months, usually, while their normal littermates lived one and a half to two years), but they were unable to reproduce themselves. This problem of short supply was solved by transplanting the ovaries of Funnyfoot females into non-Funnyfoot females, who then produced a goodly percentage of dystrophic children. These mice are now being used in medical research centers not only in the hope that they will aid in obtaining an understanding of this disease but in the further hope that they may be useful in helping to find a cure for it. In addition to her responsibilities in obtaining a supply of these mice for research institutions, Dr. Russell wanted to find out how the genes transmitted the disease. Studies at the Jackson

Laboratory in which she has had a big part indicate that muscular dystrophy is inherited by action of a single pair of recessive genes.

In 1954, when the laboratory at Bar Harbor celebrated the twenty-fifth aniversary of its founding, Dr. Russell was serving a term as Staff Scientific Director and organized the symposium on "Twenty-Five Years of Progress in Mammalian Genetics and Cancer." More than two hundred scientists interested in genetics and sciences related to it attended, many of them contributing papers she later edited for publication. This whole event increased her growing feeling that material on mammalian physiological genetics ought to be collated in a comprehensive monograph. In September, 1958, she was able to embark upon this project with substantial aid from a Guggenheim Fellowship.

An undertaking of this kind enables a scientist to become familiar at firsthand with work, ideas, and techniques in laboratories other than his own and provides a valuable perspective in planning future researches. When Dr. Russell's work on this new project is completed, it will, of course, be useful for her own personal purposes. Also it will be useful for a course to be given at the Jackson Laboratory to graduate research students in this field. But it will doubtless have a far wider application than that. She believes, from what she has experienced while collaborating with biochemists and other scientists outside her own field, that the approach of mammalian physiological genetic studies has a great deal to offer for the solution of human medical problems.

At this point in her life Elizabeth Russell seems to be

only midway in her work as a geneticist, with the possibility of nearly a quarter of a century of active life ahead of her. Her name is known, her work respected, by older leaders in her profession. She is frequently called upon for papers and discussions at meetings, where she has original ideas to contribute. She is a Fellow of the American Academy of Arts and Sciences, one of a very limited number of women scientists to whom this honor has been granted. Descendant of two families—the Buckleys and the Shulls—who have contributed much to American science, she is carrying on the tradition. Yet when asked how much of her choice of work was due to her genes, she emphasizes, "Let's not forget that any child reared in a home where the parents are scientists learns before he is able to read that science is a fascinating subject. That must have a lot to do with his choice."

RACHEL FULLER BROWN

(1898–   )

•••

Co-discoverer, with Elizabeth L. Hazen, of a valuable
antibiotic whose royalties are all used for furthering
scientific investigations

W HEN RACHEL BROWN looks back over her life, it always
seems a miracle that she ever got to college. Hers was a
family without a financial backlog that could be used for
education. Early in life her mother was left with two
children to support, and it soon became apparent
that she would not be able to supply the money for Rachel and her younger brother to go through college.
Nevertheless, Mrs. Brown was ambitious for her children,
and by the time her daughter was graduating from high
school she was aiding, as best she could, Rachel's efforts
to secure a loan, a scholarship, part-time work—anything
she could find that would make Mount Holyoke possible.
A scholarship won by high marks was a help. Then,
stimulated surely by Rachel's high scholastic record, her

efforts, and determination to go to college, a wealthy friend of Mrs. Brown's mother offered to assume complete responsibility for the girl's college education. She did it on so generous a scale that Rachel had everything a Mount Holyoke student of her day could desire—far more than many of her fellow students.

Miracle though it seems to Dr. Brown now that a fairy godmother should have waved a wand that showered funds for college over her particular head, the fact that she herself has become a wand-waving godmother, and on a much more lavish scale, seems even more surprising. "I never dreamed I would ever be in such a position," she says. It is easy to see why this is true. The science graduate who takes a civil-service position in a state Department of Health and stays in civil service throughout her work life is not expecting to become rich or even well to do. In Dr. Brown's case it appears that wealth was of so little importance to her that when opportunity for it knocked on her door, she had no interest in opening the door and saying, "Come in."

That opportunity arrived through discovery of a new type of antibiotic that proved to be so useful to mankind that it had considerable commercial value. By that time she was in her fifties and had been carrying heavy responsibilities, financial and otherwise, for some twenty-five years, for others as well as for herself. Her salary had climbed the civil-service scale from one of its lower to one of its higher grades for scientific work, in the period when even top-level civil-service scientists became talked about as a group of greatly underpaid government workers. She had found her salary sufficient to provide a good life of the kind she preferred, and she now found she wanted nothing more in the way of money for herself.

As Rachel Brown views it, "If you have enough, why should you want more?" With eyes wide open as to what she was doing, and quite likely against the advice of many friends and acquaintances when they learned about it, she chose not to accept any share of royalties from the patent rights for nystatin, of which she was co-discoverer. Its other discoverer, Elizabeth Hazen, did the same.

Of course neither Dr. Brown nor Dr. Hazen acted carelessly about what was going to happen to profits from the manufacture of nystatin that might normally be expected to go to those who discover and hold patents on a commercially valuable pharmaceutical product. They asked the Research Corporation to handle patent work, to grant licenses to pharmaceutical companies to manufacture the product on a royalty basis, and to see to it that royalties were intelligently used for the advancement of science. It is not unusual for scientists to turn to the Research Corporation for this type of service. Since its establishment in 1912 by the gift of patent rights worth millions of dollars by Frederick G. Cottrell, this corporation has handled hundreds of patents for individual scientists and inventors and for educational institutions when discoveries made by members of their staffs become the property of the institution. In most cases, however, when individuals have the right to patent their own discovery or invention, a percentage—sometimes only a small percentage but a definite share, nevertheless—of the royalties is assigned to the patent holders. With the

Hazen-Brown patent the discoverers refused to take any share at all.

The story of Rachel Brown is an American success story that reveals qualities in human beings that ought to make us hopeful about the potentialities of the human race. In Springfield, Massachusetts, where she was born, and in Webster Groves, Missouri, where her father's business had taken them and where the family lived for the first-grade-through-grammar-school period of Rachel's life, she seems to have been a child with no more promise than that of some of the other children with whom she mingled and went to school. Together with some of her small friends she came to know an ex-high-school principal from Albany, New York, who had retired to Webster Groves with a microscope, an interest in science and in young people. Rachel became interested, as countless children before and since then have been interested, in bugs. Her interest included every kind of bug in or near Webster Groves. She made a collection of them, and Mr. Onderdonk taught her how to mount them properly. Then he gave her a bottle of cyanide of her own with proper instructions, "Don't smell it," while using it on her specimens. She enjoyed this work and she enjoyed seeing all kinds of things under Professor Onderdonk's microscope. But the experience seems to have been a child's pleasure which made no noticeable impression on her other than to turn her young mind to science momentarily.

With her mother and brother, then, she returned to Springfield in time to enter the freshman class at Central High. She liked all her studies and felt no particular attraction toward any one of them. Except for a semester's course in general science she had no chemistry or physics, though she did have both fun and interest in performing some home experiments in chemistry made possible by the gift of a Bunsen burner from an uncle. When the time came at Mount Holyoke for the decision, she chose history as her college major.

Before very long, however, something began to happen that eventually caused Rachel Brown to change her mind a little and add to her major. She became aware that chemistry, quite as much as if not more than history, was catching hold of her interest. Definitely "I liked it, though even today I can't be sure why, unless it was because of its ordered pattern and precision."

Mount Holyoke had (as it has today) an excellent chemistry department. Under the influence of its staff, headed by an outstanding teacher, Dr. Emma Carr, Rachel Brown decided to take chemistry as a co-major with history, and received her A.B. in history and chemistry in 1920. Dr. Carr urged her to go to her own alma mater, the University of Chicago, for a Master's degree, and the magic wand waved once more to provide funds for a year of advanced study. But Miss Brown helped herself financially at this point, too. She served as a laboratory assistant while earning her M.S. at Chicago.

Then she was on her own—though at this point with financial responsibility only for herself. Like many young college women of her day she had been preparing to teach. She found a position at the Francis Shimer School, a preparatory school and—at that time—junior college for girls near Chicago, but soon discovered she did not want to make a lifework out of this type of teaching and living. After three years she returned to the university with a fellowship and enough money, she hoped, to see her through the two years of work necessary for her Ph.D. in organic chemistry. Though the magic wand would gladly have helped here, too, Miss Brown had matured to the point where she preferred to be on her own.

At this period of her life she met up with a very real block. The two years for which she had money were not overlong for all the work required for her doctorate as it was laid out. Actually, what was stated as her requirements was more than usual for a Ph.D. candidate in chemistry, for she had elected a minor in bacteriology which required very nearly as much work as is necessary for a Master's degree in that science, too. She worked very hard in those two years and seemed, at their end, to have accomplished all predetermined requirements. She had taken and passed all courses and presented her thesis as had been agreed upon. Only acceptance of the thesis and, then, the difficult oral examination remained. For some reason still unknown to her, acceptance of the thesis was delayed and the orals could not, of course, be given until it was accepted.

She herself could find no academic or other flaw in her position. But while, restlessly, she waited for her professor's decision, two things happened. Her money gave out and, drawing nearer in the offing was need for her to assume financial responsibility for her mother and grandmother. Through a friend she already had an offer of a position as assistant chemist in the Division of Laboratories and Research of the New York State Department of Health in Albany. The position did not depend upon whether or not she had her doctorate. Under stress of necessities facing her, she packed her bag and left Chicago. And that, for the moment, had to be the end of her Ph.D.

Seven years later, after she had done work of enough importance to be in Chicago to participate in a meeting of scientists, the professor who had delayed acceptance of her thesis got in touch with her to suggest that, "If you can stay in Chicago for a week," she take her orals in the field in which she had been doing her recent researches and was, of course, well prepared. She stayed, took and passed her orals, the earlier thesis was accepted and she received her Ph.D. seven years after she had expected it.

The work she had been doing at Albany was in the chemistry of microörganisms. Scientific work at the Health Department Laboratory included the normal services required at such laboratories, two of which were: examination of specimens sent by doctors for aid in diagnosing disease; and making vaccines, antitoxins, and serums for fighting diseases. In that pre-penicillin era pneumonia was a top killer disease treated—and often with considerable success—by injections of antiserums. Many different serums were essential because the germs that caused pneumonia (pneumococci) were of a variety of types, and a serum that was very effective for one type could be completely ineffective on another type. Physicians needed to know the type of pneumonia each patient had and be able to procure a standardized serum effective against each type.

Dr. Brown's work was to extract the specific carbohydrate which identifies each type of pneumococcus so that it could be used in standardizing the various pneumonia serums prepared for distribution to physicians. Much of her published work during her first fifteen to twenty years in Albany described facets of the chemistry of pneumococci. To explain a little about the work in which she was taking part:

For any type of pneumococcus being studied, horses or rabbits were injected with that type of germ. After a period of time blood was taken from these immunized animals and serum drawn from it. When this serum, in standardized form, was injected in human beings suffering from the same type of pneumonia caused by the type of germs injected into the animal, the antibodies in the injected serum battled against the pneumococci that were threatening the sick person's life. Dr. Brown's job was to solve some of the many chemical problems involved in standardizing the various types of serums patients needed.

The total aim involved in all this work was to enable any physician to have a patient's specimen analyzed quickly and then, depending upon whether the pneumococcus proved to be of Type I, II, VIII or what have you (eventually up to forty types, and many sub-types were studied), to have an accurately set and standardized serum quickly available with specific dosages indicated. When penicillin was discovered and proved effective against most (though not all) types of pneumonia, pneumonia serums lost their importance. But penicillin did not become available to the public until the 1940's—after Dr.

Brown had been at the Albany laboratory for fifteen years.

Her work in this period, during which she moved up a couple of notches in civil service rank (she attained the rank of senior biochemist in 1936, but her present rank of associate biochemist was not attained for another fifteen years), was not confined to pneumococci. Some of her laboratory's day-by-day problems in the chemistry of other microörganisms came to her, too, and reports on her studies into some of them appeared in scientific journals in the 1930's and '40's. Along with assigned work she was given great freedom to turn to problems of her own choice, too. It was this freedom of choice that was to bring the greatest benefits to human beings in the end and, with them, greater opportunity for other scientists to work on problems of their own choice, too.

In exercising freedom of choice it was natural enough that a scientist of Dr. Brown's experience should become interested in antibiotics. Her field was the chemistry of microörganisms and antibiotics are chemical substances obtained from microörganisms. Pencillin (1941) had proved to be a miracle worker indeed, and streptomycin (1944), scarcely less so. Chloromycetin and aureomycin soon followed, each of them bringing relief to human beings from more and more diseases. Unfortunately, though, as antibiotics became more widely available and physicians made greater and greater use of them, unpleasant results often accompanied miraculous cures—results so uncomfortable that patients sometimes complained the cure was worse than the disease.

An example of an uncomfortable result some of us

may have come across in family or friends is the painfully sore mouth that sometimes follows heavy doses of an antibiotic. This is caused by a rampant growth of fungi in the mucous membranes. The explanation for its occurrence is that one function of certain bacteria in our bodies is to control the growth of fungi, and since antibiotics killed many types of bacteria but did not kill fungi, they often killed the bacteria necessary for control of fungi. When this happens the fungi may multiply phenomenally and result in a disease physicians called moniliasis; for patients this is a sore mouth that makes eating a nightmare.

This is only one of numerous examples of how fungi can cause illness. So many examples became common after use of antibiotics in heavy doses that some of our research scientists were hunting an antibiotic that would fight fungi as other antibiotics were fighting bacteria, and be harmless to human beings.

In the latter 1940's Dr. Brown and Dr. Hazen, a microbiologist at the State Laboratory, decided to join the hunt for an antifungal antibiotic. Reviewing the knowledge available at that time they made careful decisions about how they would go about their search. Dr. Hazen had already made investigations of the actinomycetes (ac-tin-o-MY-cetes), those moldlike microörganisms found in soils from which various antibiotics had been obtained. She had gathered many soil samples from likely sources, isolated actinomycetes, and tested them to see if any of them were antagonistic to types of fungi known to make people ill. In this work she had found a number of promising microörganisms. But if the work of isolating the antibiotic from any of these microörganisms and learning if it could become of benefit to human beings was to be done, a properly trained biochemist would have to carry on from this point.

With this type of co-operation in view the search for an antifungal antibiotic began. Of many soil samples from various sources, one collected near the barn at the edge of a grazing pasture on a dairy farm in Virginia yielded the most promising actinomycete. Tests showed it was not only antifungal but was different in properties from any other actinomycete in the literature. With Dr. Hazen's isolation of the actinomycete achieved, the next step would be to see if Dr. Brown could isolate the antibiotic from the actinomycete. At this point they knew an antifungal antibiotic was present, but that was far from enough to promise success in getting what they wanted. It is not uncommon for an antibiotic that promises success to become worthless because it loses its active capacities in the course of purification. Also, antifungal agents had already been isolated, only to prove too severely toxic for human use.

The method Dr. Brown used for isolation of the antibiotic began, to touch briefly upon its high points, by taking broth cultures of the actinomycete and straining out the surface growth (called the pellicle) after five or six days, to eliminate many impurities. Tests were made which revealed not one but two antifungal agents, one in the broth and one in the pellicle. Later they recognized that with less adequate examination at this point they might have missed success in their undertaking. They stopped here long enough for Dr. Brown to learn

definitely how these two agents differed, then the decision
was made to continue with the one found in the pellicle.
From this point on the problem of isolating the antifungal agent was not simple, even for a properly qualified
biochemist. As one step, a solvent (methanol) was used
in which the antibiotic dissolved while other factors did
not dissolve. In the end Dr. Brown obtained a fine yellow powder, and finally small crystals which they tenta-
tively designated as *fungicidin* and began to test in mice.

By the early autumn of 1950 Drs. Hazen and Brown
were able to announce at a New York State meeting of
the National Academy of Sciences that they had successfully produced two antifungal agents from a soil actinomycete, one of which differed from all other antibiotics
of which they had any knowledge. In tests already made
it had been effective against large numbers of fungi and,
even in high concentrations, showed little activity against
some of the common bacteria attacked by other antibiotics. Tests within the laboratory on harmful fungi
similar to some of those that afflict human beings had
been so promising, they stated, that it warranted further
studies into its therapeutic properties for human beings
—a type of investigation necessitating medically trained
personnel.

That announcement, made in Schenectady, was sufficient to bring immediate telephone calls and correspondence with offers from pharmaceutical houses
equipped to carry on further investigations and to manufacture the product—or better, to produce it—for antibiotics are derived from living organisms grown in huge
fermentation tanks. It looked as if two civil-service sci-

entists had a patentable product that might have high commercial value. Since each of them knew she did not want to make money out of their discovery for her own use, and since help from the pharmaceutical industry was essential for further research, testing, producing, and marketing, they turned to the Research Corporation for the kind of help it was equipped to offer in circumstances of this nature.

In a short period this experienced corporation had taken over work on the management of the pending Hazen-Brown patent for what proved to be the first effective and safe antifungal antibiotic. By this time its discoverers had decided upon a permanent name for it— nystatin (ny-STA'-tin), with its first letters honoring New York State in whose laboratories the work had been done. A license for using the patent was issued by the corporation to E. R. Squibb and Sons, in whose laboratories production work soon began. Serious difficulties appeared, as they so often do when commercial scale production of chemical substances is attempted, but they were solved with the help of the Squibb Institute for Medical Research. As quickly as was safely possible, the medical profession began to co-operate in testing the effects of nystatin on patients.

Not only did it prove to be effective against a number of diseases due to pathogenic fungi of various types, but nystatin was singularly nontoxic for human beings. Administered alone or in union with other antibiotics, many conditions from which sick people had been suffering were prevented or cured. In short, a quick market was available for nystatin as soon as its harmlessness in medical practice was established.

Some idea of its widespread usefulness may be gained from figures published by the Research Corporation in its annual report for the first year (1957) in which royalties from the nystatin patent are presented. Some $135,000 had been available that first year—a figure indicating it will probably be only a few years until the first million dollars in royalties will have been distributed.

By agreement between the corporation and nystatin's discoverers all royalties are to be used to further research in the natural sciences. Half of them will be distributed through grants made by the corporation in the same way its other funds are distributed for furtherance of investigations in scientific fields. The other half will be distributed by a committee of the Brown-Hazen Fund (on which Dr. Brown and Dr. Hazen now serve) for supporting fundamental studies in biochemistry, immunology, and microbiology, with special emphasis on affording advanced scientific training for the staff of the New York State Division of Laboratories and Research. Already Dr. Brown has had the pleasant experience of having some of nystatin's royalties used by people whose problems and talents she knows intimately. But all this has made no perceptible difference in her own life. Her work at the laboratory continues much as usual, with special interest on research problems.

Her life outside the laboratory also continues much as usual—the life she had found good enough as it was without adding to it what extra money could provide. One of the things she had done as soon as she was able, after taking on financial responsibility for her mother and grandmother, was to buy a home, with a business woman friend, big enough to provide space for the four of them indoors and for a lawn and growing flowers outdoors. It was a totally adult setup, and likely to continue so, but the Episcopal Church of which she was a member had young people who needed Sunday school teachers, and she became one of those teachers. This provided young people in plenty, and the result of those contacts has been that, after enough years had passed, she found herself invited to inspect new homes and soon to attend baptisms. She has quite a family by this time, and it keeps growing. For the last few years she has been teaching ten-year-olds, an age group she enjoys.

After the death of her grandmother there was an empty bedroom just at the moment when the personnel director at the laboratory was trying to find a home for a young Chinese physician who had been assigned to observe methods at the laboratory for a few months. The experience of sharing their home with a young Chinese woman was so rewarding that Dr. Brown considered herself fortunate when a second Chinese woman, who has continued her scientific work in Albany ever since, was available for the room just as its earlier occupant was leaving it. Each young woman had members of her own family, and Chinese friends, studying in America, and the Brown-Wakerley home was opened to all of them it could accommodate. Since about 1946 it has been filled with Chinese students who return to it a couple of times a year as naturally as their American classmates go to their own homes for college vacations. Cots have been provided for the overflow that keeps occurring. Easter week of 1958 found seven visiting Chinese spending their vacation at the house on Buckingham Drive in Albany and, "I just loved having them—I always do," was Rachel Brown's reaction to it—especially to the children who by this time have been born to members of the group here in America. A collapsible gate at the top of the stairs and a rocking horse in front of the living-room fireplace are now part of her standard home equipment.

To know Rachel Brown is to know that science is a field in which human beings may, if they will, develop standards and values that are not measured by a materialistic yardstick. Nor need the development of these standards deter a scientist from attaining distinction and honor in professional life. But more than scientific distinction, more than the honorary Phi Beta Kappa and special citation from Mount Holyoke, this warm and modest woman of science derives her deepest satisfaction from knowing that her work has helped to save lives and relieve human suffering.

CHIEN SHIUNG WU

(1915–   )

• •

Nuclear physicist whose work helped overthrow an erroneous concept hitherto accepted in all theories of the physical structure of the universe

ONE OF THE MOST distinguished women of science in America today is a Chinese woman, Dr. Chien Shiung (pronounced Chen Shung) Wu, professor of physics at Columbia University. Superlatives should be attributed cautiously when applying them to scientists. With this in mind, it is no exaggeration to say that in the physical sciences Dr. Wu stands definitely among the top few women in the world today. When Princeton University, in the spring of 1958, gave her the first honorary doctorate in science it had ever bestowed upon a woman, its President declared that she had "richly earned the right to be called the world's foremost female experimental physicist."

Though the quality of her scientific work has earned

for her a professorial rank rarely accorded women in outstanding American nuclear physics centers today, Dr. Wu
wears it all lightly and unassumingly. Small enough to
be described as petite, she dresses in the slit-skirt Chinese
garb that becomes her well. It is a form of dress which,
whether or not it is concealed beneath the laboratory
coat of the research scientist, indicates her deep and enduring ties to the land of her birth. She is a true daughter
of her people.

Yet in the startling vitality of her handshake lies a
warmth and communicativeness that transcends race and
nationality. A human being of deep womanly reserve,
that handshake casts aside all artificial reservations to get
at realities. It becomes a challenge for the layman in
science to cast aside his self-imposed reservations, too,
and try to approach her science with a completely open
mind. If he can do this, he may find a bridge of understanding is possible between his mind and the nuclear
scientist whose work he usually makes no great effort to
understand.

True, nuclear physics is one of the most abstract and
complicated of the sciences to a layman. Yet the fact that
modern music is one of the most abstract and complicated
of the arts has not prevented many laymen from finding
new meaning and beauty in some, at least, of this music
which they first rejected as incomprehensible noise. In
science as in art understanding arrives as a result of intelligent effort. With that effort we find ourselves a little
more at home in realms in which we first wandered about
as complete strangers. Admittedly it is not easy for the

adult laymen to take first steps toward what he does not understand. Young people do this more easily. Yet for people of any age whose minds are not set in rigid molds, for those who have not too long suppressed their imaginations, it is possible to take first steps toward a beginning understanding of the invisibles, called atoms, that constitute our bodies and all else confronting our eyes.

After all, most of us had the experience, in high school days, of seeing two invisible gases (hydrogen and oxygen) become visible water as they were united in a laboratory test tube. That type of experience can spur our imaginations, as we look at a glass of water today, to an attempt to comprehend that both the glass and the water are built of invisibles that have somehow combined and become visible. When we make the attempt to comprehend that the glass as well as the water is composed of invisibles called atoms, imagination has helped us take a first step in atomic physics.

Nor is it hard for the layman who has taken his first leap into the dark successfully to take the second step, which leads into Dr. Wu's specific field of nuclear physics—that is, the physics of the nucleus, or core, of the atom. This step happens when, again consciously or unconsciously, our minds attempt to comprehend that each invisible atom* in the glass and in the water is composed of smaller invisible constituents—of postive and negative electrical charges called protons and electrons, of neutrons which are without any charge at all, of unstable particles called mesons, and of K-mesons, which

---

* To refresh your mind on the size of the atom, see Lise Meitner's graphic description of it in the footnote on page 25.

were discovered as recently as 1952-53, and which decay into sometimes two and sometimes three pi-mesons.

To try to admit all this past the door of our minds, to accept the idea of invisible constituents of invisible atoms as a fact, is not too difficult. But—and this is a big *but*— when the layman attempts to follow the work of scientists who contrive apparatuses that put these invisibles through antics like performing fleas, he is lost. At such a point, if he really is interested enough to want to understand more but is not certain he has the innate capacity to do so, he may take comfort from the life stories of some of our distinguished contemporary scientists. Some of them, even some who have gone far and achieved greatly in the field of nuclear physics, grew up without any assurance or knowledge that they possessed this capacity either.

Chien Shiung Wu, however, was not such a person. As a child in China she knew she wanted to be a scientist, though her dreams never carried her to a physics laboratory at Columbia University in America or anywhere else. Nor did she tinker with homemade radio sets as did many scientifically inclined American youngsters of her era. She was just a happy little girl in a Chinese home in Liu Ho, a small town near Shanghai where she had been born, enjoying the kind of life other little girls of her social group in China enjoyed. In one respect, though, her life differed from that of many other young people in her community. Her father, Wu Zong-Yee, was the principal of a school in Liu Ho. Being a scholar as well as the type of father he was, Chien Shiung and her two brothers were surrounded in their home with books they were encouraged to read. Though she was a child who loved to play, she needed no urging to read. Both as a student in her father's school and in her home she imbibed from books and her surroundings the traditional culture of her native land and an enduring respect for it—respect for the old ways, for older people, for Chinese classics and for the art and music of old China.

"It was a wonderfully happy life. I had a fortunate and happy childhood," she says today.

Her father was a man far in advance of his time. Even as he taught schoolchildren respect for true values in the old ways he taught them respect for values in modern life and ideas as well. He wanted to prepare children for the modern life into which they would be plunged by grounding them deeply in the true values of their Chinese heritage which could enrich life in any era. The days of the Old Empress and her successor were gone. Wu Zong-Yee recognized changes coming to the Orient. He wanted to prepare young people for them, though few in Liu Ho were in step with him.

When Chien Shiung had completed the schooling available in her community, she was sent to Soochow for high-school work. Several things happened during her school days there that were going to be of importance in her life. First, she began to study English, a language that would be very helpful, even essential, to her later. More important, she decided to become a physicist. No dramatic moment or event occurred to mark in her memory the time of this decision. She wanted higher education—in this she was the true daughter of her father. She liked her studies, and as she continued her high-school work, she became aware that she had a greater affinity for some subjects than for others. Certainly she liked mathematics and science. Then she reached physics and, "Somehow I soon knew it was what I wanted to go on with." Something inside told her so, she says, but little did she know then how definitely she had recognized a truth that some process inside her had brought to a consciousness in her mind.

With the decision about her future work made, she took the next natural step after graduation from the Soochow High School by enrolling as a student at the government-supported National Central University at Nanking. Nanking was then the capital of the Nationalist Government and, like all eastern China, in a very unsettled condition, but student life went on much as usual. Miss Wu took all the math and physics available, enjoyed the intellectual cameraderie with fellow students that was usual in a Chinese University, and received her bachelorate in science in 1936.

She now wanted and was ready for graduate study in physics, which China did not offer. Her parents were easily persuaded to let her come to America for this purpose, so the fall of 1936 found her at the University of California in Berkeley, where Dr. Ernest Lawrence had just been made the director of the radiation laboratory. Here this American born and educated physicist would be working on the development of his invention, an atom-smashing cyclotron, and pursuing researches in atomic structure and transmutations which brought him the Nobel Prize in Physics while Miss Wu was studying under him. Truly, any young scientist interested in nuclear physics was fortunate in having chosen Dr. Lawrence's laboratories for graduate study at that particular time. Once she had been accepted as a graduate student, everything depended upon whether her Chinese university education and her own abilities would measure up to the work demanded in this graduate center where some of the finest minds in nuclear physics were working.

Her need to adjust to American university life and methods came simultaneously with a need to adjust to American life outside the classroom and laboratory. At International House, where she lived with other students from the Orient and from all over Europe as well, she found quick and understanding help. In time she learned to like American cooking—or some of it—and the social life, with the exception of dancing, enjoyed by the young people at International House. In time, too, she learned to like the classical music of the West, and its folk songs. The fellow graduate student of physics at Berkeley, Luke Cha-Liou Yuan, who became her husband after she had been in this country a few years, is a music lover who enjoys playing as well as listening to both Oriental and Occidental music, and their home is a place where both types are often heard.

Whatever her few early difficulties may have been in making her adjustments to American life outside the university, no one had need to worry about her studies. She stood up to the strenuous graduate work demanded at the University of California and was given a teaching assistantship at the beginning of her second semester's work; it was renewed each year to carry her through the Ph.D. in nuclear physics she received in 1940. The investigations Miss Wu made in preparation for her doctor's thesis were in two parts. In one study, which dealt with the X-radiations from beta decay, she showed ingenuity in creating new methods for separating two types of rays during disintegration, and was able to show good agreement between the experimental results and the theoretical predictions. The other study, undertaken immediately after the fission of uranium had been announced at Berkeley, was on radioactive noble gases from uranium fission. Collaborating with Dr. E. Segré, they were able to establish "two complete chains of radioactive decay with the half lives, radiations and isotope numbers completely identified." This work was withheld from publication until the war was over, but was transmitted, by request, to the Los Alamos Laboratories.

Obviously Dr. Wu had begun to show brilliance in her field of nuclear physics before she had completed work for her doctorate. She was elected to Phi Beta Kappa for outstanding work as a graduate student and the university made a position available to her as Dr. Lawrence's research assistant in the Radiation Laboratory. Since the war situation in China was going from bad to worse, she accepted it, and her researches in pure science continued for a period. Then pure research was pushed aside in her laboratory for defense research and, in 1942, Dr. Wu came East to teach physics at Smith College.

As her first year at Smith was drawing to a close, something happened that indicates she must unquestionably have exhibited, in her work with Dr. Lawrence, abilities still rare among physicists. Princeton University called her—a young woman of only twenty-seven—to its campus to teach nuclear physics to its men students. Dr. Wu, who says one of the greatest oddities she had found in America (one that still surprises her as a negation of the American ideal of equality) was the fact that some of our best institutions of higher learning do not accept women students, explains this offer from Princeton with the words, "The war was on and there was a shortage of available physics teachers." This is her characteristic modesty. Yet obviously young Dr. Chien Shiung Wu, only a year out of Dr. Lawrence's laboratories, had something outstanding to offer to the type of university equipped with the expensive apparatus necessary for nuclear research.

She accepted the Princeton offer, but her time there was short. After only a few months a call came saying she was needed for work on the Manhattan Project at Columbia University. To accept this offer would enable her to make a more direct contribution to the war effort, which was what she wanted more than anything else at that moment. So in March, 1944, she became a member of the scientific staff of the Division of War Research at Columbia, where, until the end of the war, her major effort was spent in the development of instruments for the detection of radiation. One of her achievements here was perfection of a method of fusing a thin mica window to a Geiger counter.

Soon after the war was over Dr. Wu became a Research Associate at Columbia and found opportunity to continue her studies in beta decay, the field in which she had worked in California. Theories existed about beta decay, but theories always need proof—or disproof—and techniques for beta spectroscopy were so primitive in 1946 that a vast discrepancy existed between theory and experimental results in this field. In her Columbia laboratory she set about her attempt to bridge this seemingly unsurmountable discrepancy by finding new methods of studying the shapes of beta spectra and the interaction of beta decay. In order to accomplish study of the spectra, she devised a technique in which a scintillation counter and beta detector were used inside a magnetic spectrometer. These studies continued for a number of years at Columbia. They gave convincing proof of the Fermi theory of beta decay, and proof of her growing stature as a competent physicist. They also helped win her promotion to associate professor of physics at Columbia in 1952.

Graduate students working with Dr. Wu were having opportunity to take part in some of the top-ranking work in experimental physics being done in America. One after another, problems in beta decay, of annihilation radiation, and radiation detection devices were studied. She was surprised herself, along with her students, at some of the results that came as her gifted mind found new ways and means to perform experimental work that was being followed with interest by other physicists. And in 1956 the opportunity came that would enable her to co-operate creatively with two young Chinese-American physicists in work whose results brought world-wide acclaim to American science and the Nobel Prize in Physics to the two young men.

These two, Professors Tsung Dao Lee of Columbia and Chen Ning Yang of the Institute for Advanced Study at Princeton, had been among the small group of theoretical physicists who, by the middle of 1946, had begun to express doubt of the universal validity of a concept, known as the principle of parity, that had been accepted as a fundamental law of physics by all theoretical physicists for some thirty years. This law had been built into all physical theories for three decades. So universally had it been accepted it was almost as unthinkable for a scientist to cast doubt on the principle of parity as on the law of gravitation.

Yet a few had begun to doubt. One reason for their doubts was because observations made on the disintegration of K-mesons (discovered 1952-53) were baffling to scientists versed in what ought to happen in their disintegration according to the principle of parity. Drs. Lee and Yang took up the challenge and plunged into a systematic investigation of the status of all experimental knowledge concerning the phenomenon known as parity and were surprised to find loopholes in it. Knowledge on which the validity of the principle rested was not complete. So they boldly asserted that the parity principle was in error and proposed two different types of experiments to test their hypothesis, one with pi and muon mesons and one with beta rays. Dr. Wu undertook the task of experimentation on this crucial test with beta rays.

To explain a little about the law of parity: According to this law, in the nuclear world an object and its mirror image behave in the same way. To get the idea of the behavior of a mirror image, place yourself in front of a mirror with a corkscrew in one hand and a corked bottle in the other. Revolve the corkscrew in a clockwise motion until the cork comes out of the bottle. In the mirror the motion becomes counterclockwise—and the cork comes out of the bottle. Yet if you tried the counterclockwise motion in the cork itself the screw would not work its way into the cork. Its behavior would be different from the way it appeared in the mirror.

The law of parity held that, in invisible nuclear structures, the *actual* behavior of object and mirror image is identical. Dr. Wu's experiment was, so to speak, to see if, in nuclear structures, the cork actually did come out of the bottle (that is, the particles fly off from the nucleus during decay) regardless of the direction of the turn of the screw (spin of the nucleus).

It was a complex and extremely difficult experiment and certainly not to be understood by the uninitiated. She asked for collaboration from the National Bureau of Standard's Low Temperature Physics Group and, with the help of specialists in radioactive measurements at the National Bureau of Standards and partial support from the Atomic Energy Commission, set about one of the most intricate experiments posed by modern physics. Briefly, a radioactive nucleus of cobalt 60 was placed in a complex cooling and vacuum system capable of reaching a temperature of 0.01 degrees above absolute zero (absolute zero is −459 degrees Fahrenheit), at which temperature thermal motion is so greatly reduced that the spinning cobalt nuclei can, through the application of a magnetic field, be aligned like little magnets parallel to the magnetic field. Included in the apparatus with the cooling system was a device—a scintillation counter—that counted the electrons emitted by the aligned cobalt nuclei as they disintegrated.

When the count was in, the law of parity was out. The number of electrons emitted in the opposite direction of the spin was greater than the number emitted along the direction of the spin—so much greater that it was clearly evident that electrons greatly favored shooting off in the opposite direction of the spin axis of cobalt 60. Their direction seemed to be predetermined for them as the thread of a corkscrew predetermines whether motion must be applied to the right or to the left. (A "left-handed" corkscrew can be made, of course, that extracts a cork by a counterclockwise turn.) As the scientist puts it, the experiment Dr. Wu and her collaborators successfully performed indicates that electrons have a "handedness." Elementary particles must be spoken of as right-handed or left-handed. They advance along an axis of rotation in either a right-handed or left-handed manner, and are emitted in opposite directions dictated by the motion of their rotation, or spin.

High honors came to Dr. Wu as the importance of her work in proving the theory for which two of her fellow countymen received the Nobel Prize in Physics became known. In addition to the Princeton honorary degree mentioned earlier, she became the seventh woman member of our National Academy of Sciences in its near-century of existence, was appointed to a full professorship at Columbia, and was elected to membership in the Academia Sinica (Academy of Sciences of China). In March, 1958, she spoke to the National Science Award students in Washington, and the main message she left them was to urge them to dare to doubt. "The over-throw of the parity law drives home again the idea that science is not static, but ever-growing and dynamic," she told them. "It is the courage to doubt what has long been established, the incessant search for its verification and proof that pushed the wheel of science forward."

One of her own doubts, as she works in her university's classrooms and laboratories with graduate students and finds so many of the women among them from other lands, is whether America is nurturing and developing abilities in physics in its young women. She cannot understand why so few young American women are at-tracted to physics. She cannot believe talent for it is lack-ing in them when it appears so often in young women of other cultures. She thinks it is unwise to continue atti-tudes in either social or intellectual life that throttle a younger generation's innate abilities. She herself, with a physicist husband and their son who will have his par-ents' best efforts to help him develop in physics or other-wise as his own abilities suggest, finds nuclear physics a satisfying field for any human being whose talents lie in this realm.

EDITH HINKLEY QUIMBY

(1891–)

•••

Physicist who helped create the new science of radiation
physics, now basic to good medical practice everywhere

THE STORY OF Edith Quimby is the story of a girl from
the Middle West who took a naturally inquiring mind
to the Far West for an education, then came East and
used it to help create the new field of scientific work
known as radiation physics. Beneficial results of that
work reach into every community in our country today.
Every time X-ray examinations of teeth or other parts of
the body are made in a dentist's or physician's office,
every time radium or radiation treatments of any kind are
given in a hospital, some aspect of Edith Quimby's contributions to the radiological science underlying them is
used. Personally, or through textbooks written in whole
or in part by her, she has probably taught as many physicians who have become specialists in radiology as any
other person in America today.

94

In 1904, when Edith Hinkley was graduated from grammar school in Rockford, Illinois, where she had been born, the possibility of using X-rays and radium in treating diseases was only beginning to be thought about—and in only a scant few of the world's medical centers. No schoolchild anywhere had a dental or chest X-ray in the routine manner experienced by many schoolchildren today. The fact that powerful rays emanated from radioactive ores in the earth's crust had been learned only a few years earlier. Their discovery would eventually give rise to new scientific knowledge that would be recorded in high-school and college textbooks everywhere. But in Boise, Idaho, where the Hinkley family moved as Edith was ready for high school, her courses in physics and chemistry—both of them very good for their day—were of the variety now spoken of as "nineteenth-century science." The radioactive age was too near its birth for its results to have reached high-school textbooks.

To some extent this was true, too, of the physics in which she majored (with a co-major in mathematics) at Whitman College in Walla Walla, Washington—though before graduation there in 1912 the laboratory work did include one experiment with radium and another with X-rays. So, except for a doggedly inquiring mind seemingly born in her, Edith Quimby might well have become one of the thousands of young high-school science teachers of her day, content to catch up with scientific progress after it had been made instead of being one of those who helped markedly to create that progress in one small but important field.

She had been fortunate as a girl in having a father who

had been sympathetic with the inquiring type of mind that appeared in his oldest child. Edith was one of those youngsters who wanted to know why, what, and when; he was one of the fathers who did not tell her to stop asking questions. He urged her to find the answers elsewhere if he could not supply them himself or if the question was one whose answer he thought she could find for herself. She was fortunate, too, in having a high-school science teacher who stimulated her interest in chemistry and physics and taught her to answer some of her questions in a laboratory. Mr. Rhodenbaugh was probably a big factor in her decision to major in physics and mathematics in college.

Then, at Whitman College, she was definitely fortunate again. Not only did she have a full tuition scholarship for four years, she was also in one of the modest-sized American co-educational colleges that specialize in good teaching by teachers who maintain close relationships with students. As a result she received her B.S. knowing she had touched only the surface in physics and wanting to know more about it. She owes a great deal to the Whitman faculty, especially to her advisor and mathematics teacher, Professor Bratton (later President of the college) and to Professor Brown, her physics teacher, who encouraged her to take the mathematics-physics major never before attempted by a woman student, and to keep on asking questions.

The Hinkleys, however, were a family in modest circumstances with other young people to be thought of. It was time for their eldest to earn her own living. Since Edith wanted and had planned to teach, she found a job as a teacher of chemistry and physics in the high school at Nyssa, Oregon. Two years later she was able to go to Berkeley with a teaching fellowship at the University of California that enabled her to support herself while working for her Master's degree in physics. At the end of her first year at the university she married a fellow graduate-student-physicist, Shirley L. Quimby. At the end of the next year she had her M.A., and the following September found them in Antioch, California, some fifty miles east of Berkeley. Here Shirley Quimby had a position teaching science in the high school and his wife settled into domesticity, including, as one of its enjoyable aspects, plenty of cooking—another field in which an intelligently inquiring mind with a kitchen as a laboratory often achieves better results than come from a get-it-out-of-a-cook-book mind.

Surely nothing in Edith Quimby's life up to this point was out of the ordinary for a smart young college graduate of her day. A gray-eyed young woman of five feet eight, of fine appearance and with a mass of blonde hair, good humored, home loving, she might have been any of hundreds of young women who were coming out of college prepared to teach, yet ready to give it up when or if the right man came along who wanted to establish a home with her in it. Nor was there anything unusual in the fact that, with America's entry into World War I that year the Quimbys were at Antioch, she should take her husband's position as a high-school science teacher when he joined the Navy. Nor that she should give up this position, join him in New England, and settle happily down to domesticity again when Shirley Quimby was retained in service for an additional year after the War was over, on submarine detection work at the Naval Base at New London, Connecticut.

When his Navy service came to an end, young Mr. Quimby wanted very much to study for his Ph.D. in physics. No G.I. Bill of Rights existed to help World War I service men finance their higher education. The best Shirley Quimby could do financially, while working for his doctorate, was a part-time instructorship that would pay him $1,000 a year while he studied. Since two people could not live and eat properly in New York City on that sum, Mrs. Quimby needed a job. They learned that the chief physicist at the New York City Memorial Hospital for Cancer and Allied Diseases, Dr. Gioacchino Failla, had recently returned from military duties in Europe and had plans for developing a radiological research laboratory at this hospital. They learned, too, that he needed an assistant physicist, and someone who knew Edith Quimby's qualifications spoke to Dr. Failla about her.

To engage a woman for such a position was a rather novel idea. No woman in America was engaged in medical physical research at that time. But Edith Quimby had the right educational background in physics and Dr. Failla had no prejudices about working with women. She got the job, started to work with him in 1919, and their scientific collaboration has continued ever since.

No such science as radiological physics existed as these two began their work, even though radiotherapy—that is, the use of X-rays and radium for the treatment of disease —was being practiced in a number of hospitals. In the right physician's hands it was proving to be a powerful weapon, even though, with the apparatus and techniques available, it was not without dangers both for patients and for those administering the treatments. Into this situation the work of a few physicists, with co-operation from physicians, was projecting itself. Their purpose was to learn how to apply the laws of physics to the use of X-rays and radium on human beings and to put their findings into the hands of the medical profession.

Before much time had passed it became evident that proper radiation therapy would necessitate the training of two new types of specialists for work in the medical field—the radiotherapist and the radiation physicist. The radiotherapist would always have to be a physician, capable of diagnosing diseases and prescribing therapeutic treatments of specific dosages at specific body locations. The radiation physicist would have to be a graduate physicist, capable of measuring radiation accurately so it could be prescribed accurately by the physician, and of seeing to it that equipment used in ray treatments would give specifically prescribed doses accurately to the patient, without danger to him or to those administering them.

When Mrs. Quimby began her work as Dr. Failla's assistant physicist, radium was still so scarce and so prohibitively costly that Memorial Hospital was one of the comparatively few institutions that had enough radium and apparatus for physical research work in this field of medical investigation. The first radium produced in America had not been ready for use until 1913, and so long and difficult had been its isolation and purification from American ores that the first gram of it sold for $120,-

000. Not until 1916—only three years before Mrs. Quimby began her work—had the American Radium Society been founded by physicians (and with full membership in it open only to physicians) to "promote the scientific study of radium and other sources of ionizing radiations in relation to their physical properties and their therapeutic application."

From all this it will be seen that, with her M.A. degree and a few years' experience as a high-school teacher behind her, Mrs. Quimby, still in her twenties, had opened the door to and been accepted as a worker on the ground floor of the new science of radiology—that branch of science which deals with radiant energy and its uses in the diagnosis and treatment of disease. Twenty-one years later, with an Honorary Doctorate in Science from her alma mater already testifying to the academic world's evaluation of her scientific achievements, Dr. Edith Quimby arose in a meeting of the American Radium Society to receive its highest honor, the Janeway Medal. With the exception of Dr. Failla one year previously, she was the first person without an M.D. degree to receive this medal. She was the first and is still the only woman who has ever received it. Moreover, it would be another eleven years (1951) before this society would award full membership to anyone without an M.D. degree, even though highly qualified physicists were essential for fulfilling the society's purpose as quoted earlier from its constitution.

Specifically, what Dr. Quimby had done for twenty-one years, as assistant and then associate physicist at Memorial Hospital, was to measure the generation and penetration of various forms of radiation so as to make exact dosages in radiotherapy possible. Though physicians knew that rays penetrated the human body exposed to them and that some rays penetrated more deeply than others, no one knew exactly how deeply and over what area. A usual request from a physician to a therapist giving a radium treatment might be, "Give my patient a good dose of radiation but don't damage the skin." He did not know, often, how to be more exact than that.

What Dr. Quimby was very largely responsible for establishing was: how much radiation was emitted from a specific source, how much was delivered in the air, how much to the skin, and how much within the body, under varying conditions of irradiation. In applying, as she did, the laws of physics to reactions from radiation within the living body, she became one of our pioneer biophysicists. Between 1920-40 more than fifty papers describing her findings appeared in scientific journals. They contained practical information that might be put into immediate use wherever treatments were being given. The paper she read when she received the Janeway Medal for this work summarized these findings as of that year—1940—but her investigations and measurements would continue for years.

Many things became evident year after year as more and more physicians used radiotherapy with varying degrees of success. It is obvious even to a layman how invaluable a physicist's work could be to these medical specialists. In the early days of radiotherapy, for example, if a physician prescribed the same radiation exposure for two patients having the same type of tumor which, however, in one case was situated two centimeters beneath the skin and in the other case seven centimeters deep, he might foresee that the results of these treatments would not be the same in the two tumors. But he himself did not have the training and information to know how to vary the treatments to get the same results.

By the accurate measurements and calculations Dr. Quimby was making available, it could be demonstrated that one of these tumors might actually be receiving twice as much radiation as the other. The dose delivered to the tumor depended upon its depth below the skin, on a number of other factors such as the size of the irradiated area, the distance of the X-ray tube from the body, and so on. Once these and other facts were established, it became clear why, for example, a particular radiation exposure to a patient weighing 100 pounds might produce much more severe reactions than the same exposure to a patient weighing 170 pounds.

No wonder physicians pinned a medal on Edith Quimby after she had spent more than twenty years accumulating for them quantitative data that made it possible for them to use radiation accurately in the treatment of disease. Actually, some of these physicians did more than give her a medal; they arranged for her appointment as Assistant Professor of Radiology at Cornell Medical School, which had a close association with Memorial Hospital, where she and Dr. Failla were working.

This teaching appointment came in 1941, the year she received the Gold Medal of the Radiological Society of North America, an award no other woman except Marie Curie has, as yet, received. The citation on Dr. Quimby's award "for continuous service to radiology" stated that her work "in simplification of the problem of dosage" had placed every radiologist in her debt. It had placed countless patients in her debt, too.

With her appointment to the Cornell faculty came increased opportunity for teaching physicians, in classrooms as well as in the laboratory, the science she was helping to create. Radiology had become a speciality in medicine along with surgery, gynecology, pediatrics, and other specialties, and Dr. Quimby was better qualified than physicians to teach some of its physical aspects. An even greater opportunity came in 1943 when she was offered and accepted an associate professorship at the College of Physicians and Surgeons (known as P and S) of Columbia University, to whose staff Dr. Failla had also been called. Her full professorship in this top-ranking medical school came in 1954, the year she served as President of the American Radium Society, which had by this time taken leadership in granting equality of professional status for radiation physicists with radiologists in radiological science in this country.

As radiotherapy came more and more widely in use in hospitals, safety factors involved in treatments became of correspondingly greater importance With the increasing availability of radioisotopes for medical treatments that began in the latter 1940's, a third type of agent was added to X-rays and radium, and this also involved dangers to those who were called upon to use them. Dr. Quimby assumed responsibility for acquiring knowledge about this aspect of radiation physics, too, and set about it with a scientist's precision. As Director of the P and S

Radioisotope Laboratory she studied best ways of working with these agents at all levels. Her investigations included not only methods of handling the isotopes themselves but best practices for nurses to use in caring for patients while they are receiving this type of treatment and precautionary measures that should be taken in handling the bodies of patients who die within a short period after receiving isotope therapy. She became a recognized expert in the proper disposal of radioactive wastes occurring in hospitals, and in procedures for cleaning up if an accident resulted in radioactive spills.

Edith Quimby's is a difficult life to catch and condense in a few pages of type. Looking at it in one way, her work might be summarized by saying she has made three different types of contributions in helping to build a new science: (1) in making accurate radiation dosage for patients possible; (2) in showing how to avoid radiation hazards for all concerned with its use; and (3) in teaching the basic physics of radiation therapy to physicians who want to become radiologists. But that would be only a part of the whole story. Actually, her personality—the kind of human being she is—has been almost as important in building this science as her work. To explain:

For the nonphysician to win professional acceptance from physicians in a collaborative undertaking involving the care of the sick is not easy. The development of radiation physics as a basic component of medical practice in radiology was such an undertaking. Physicians guard their profession's prerogatives zealously, and it is right that they should. Wherever illness is concerned, the medical doctor has long assumed responsibility, and others work under his direction. Yet the field of knowledge essential to the practice of medicine today has become so vast that the individual physician cannot, with the best intentions and most studious application, learn and retain all of it.

To win recognition of the fact that radiotherapy needed co-operation between highly educated physicists and highly educated physicians without either being under the direction of the other was a task for which a definite type of personality as well as a definite type of knowledge in physics was of value. In Dr. Quimby this personality and the scientific knowledge and ability to use it were combined in one person. Over the years she, as much as any other person, won from top leaders in the medical world recognition for radiation physicists of professional equality in the field of radiotherapy.

Probably her position on a medical school faculty as a nonphysician teacher of graduate physicians studying to become specialists in radiology gave her one of her most effective tools. Physicians in her classes could be led to a realization of their need for professional help in the part of their science that involved a higher degree of mathematical and physical skill than they were likely themselves to possess.

As a result of her work and that of a few other pioneers a new professional field for the physicist in now established. The radiation physicist co-operates with physicians as they need and wish his services, but he is responsible, as they are, only to the head of his department. It is a field in which a considerable number of women are doing good work, though men are in the majority. It is one in which a Ph.D. in physics is an asset and some postgraduate work a necessity. It is one which, though limited by the number of hospitals equipped for modern radiotherapy and the number of higher educational institutions teaching it, still offers more opportunities than there are trained physicists to fill them.

Honors have come to Edith Quimby—too many to be enumerated here—and the end of them, doubtless, is not in sight. Two of the more recent of them were an honorary Doctor of Science from Rutgers University in 1956 and the Medal of the American Cancer Society in 1957. At the national level she has been singled out to serve on the Atomic Energy Commission's Committee for the Control and Distribution of Radioactive Isotopes and on the National Committee for Radiation Protection. She has long been one of the examiners for the American Board of Radiology, which accredits physicians as specialists in radiology.

Through it all and despite her many professional activities a life outside her work has always been an essential for Edith Quimby. As soon as her husband had his Ph.D. (he has been on the staff of the Department of Physics at Columbia University ever since), they found an apartment to their liking in Greenwich Village, where they still live. Here Edith Quimby has done a wife's share in creating a home and works at it regularly. That home is a center for living quite apart from her work life—a place where she reads and plays bridge, makes many of her own clothes, and enjoys preparing appetizing meals for her husband and their guests. These home tasks—the things

so many women with no work outside the home enjoy—
are her pleasures, too.

Vacation time usually takes both Quimbys out of their
home and away from New York. She and her husband
are very fond of travel and make a trip abroad almost
every year. They fly, if there is need for it, but their
preference is to board a slow ship and take their time
about getting wherever they are going. Seeing things she
has not been seeing in New York, renewing ties with
many acquaintances in Europe and Latin America, round
off an active life for this pioneer in a new realm of physics
whose work has helped open new opportunities for young
scientists today.

JOCELYN CRANE

(1909–   )

••

Zoologist whose studies of the social behavior of small
animals have taken her to tropical jungles, to mountain-
tops and to islands of the seas

SHE ALWAYS LOVED ANIMALS. The smaller the animal,
the more she seemed to love it. By the time she was six,
she knew she wanted to work with them all her life.
That memory is still clear in Jocelyn Crane's mind today.
Caterpillars fascinated her. Spiders, too. They were to
be some of the animals she would work with. And she
learned far earlier than do most people that these creatures, along with all other living organisms that are not
plants, are animals.

Anyone who knew this small girl, especially her father
and mother, soon learned what kind of book to give her
for a birthday or Christmas present. Anything about
animals pleased her and the smaller the animals, the more
she was pleased. Pictures of crabs or bees—pictures of

any little creatures she would eventually learn to call arthropods—could hold her interest indefinitely. She pored and pored over pages on which she found these fascinating little creatures with jointed appendages till she wishes today she might recall all that she thought as she pored.

When she learned to read, she was soon hunting all she could find about foreign countries. Again her parents co-operated intelligently. Asia began to fascinate her—especially its hot regions—with the same compulsion caterpillars held for her. She can never be sure whether it was Asia itself or mainly all the small animals inhabiting this continent that made her want to go there as soon as she could. Not the cold barren regions of northern China or Tibet, not Himalayan peaks that call to another type of child who wants to climb mountains, but the tropical jungles of the Orient called to Jocelyn Crane. And then she learned about the jungles of Africa and of South America, and she wanted to investigate every small living thing that inhabited the jungles of all these continents.

Rarely indeed do small children know as definitely as did Jocelyn Crane what they want to do, especially when, as in her case, no one in her family had ever done these things. Fewer still begin to do exactly what they want to do as soon as they reach an age when it is possible to begin to work at it. Still fewer know with as much assurance in middle life that what they thought they wanted to do at the age of six was exactly right for them and that no other type of work or life could have offered quite the same satisfaction. "I was one of the lucky ones," she says. She feels she scarcely needed to choose her work, but was born to fit into it.

Lucky—yes—yet Jocelyn Crane's early schooling might have been a handicap for many children destined to work in a scientific field. When she was six and ready for school, her family left St. Louis, where she had been born, and she scarcely stopped moving for the rest of her grade-school life. Her first six grades were accomplished in eleven different schools as far apart as Washington, D.C., and Los Angeles, California. She moved so often that teachers, schoolmates, classes, and buildings are understandably confused in her mind today. When she was twelve and ready for seventh grade, her mother put her in the University School for Girls in Chicago. At the end of her first year there, far from having had to catch up with girls of her age who had had the advantages of stabilized life and schooling for six years, her teachers found her ready for high-school-level work and recommended that she skip eighth grade. They were right, so Jocelyn graduated in 1926 at the age of seventeen, a year younger than the average graduate, and with the kind of marks in her college-entrance examinations that would recommend her to any college she wanted to attend.

Just as she had known at six that she wanted to work with small animals, she had known in her early teens that she wanted to go to Smith College. She has no idea how she first heard of Smith or why she wanted to go there. Her University School teachers knew she wanted to study zoology, and though no zoology existed in their curriculum by which they might have tested her abilities, they had given her physics, chemistry, and plenty of math-

ematics, which any science student needs, and accepted
the fact that they were dealing with a student who knew
what she wanted. They knew, too, that Smith offered excellent work in zoology. So in the fall of 1926 a tallish,
slender, blue-eyed blonde arrived in Northampton, knowing what she was there for even though college regulations
did not permit her to choose her major before the end
of her second year.

She could, of course, take zoology as a freshman. She
loved it and did very well at it, which scarcely surprised
her, but she made a very good record in all her other
freshman studies, too. As a sophomore she was able to
take another "zo" course, and one in astronomy—for what
jungle traveler may not someday need to know about the
stars? That year her faculty advisor suggested that she
go out for special honors in zoology, which is what she
did when she was ready for her junior year's work.

To her dying day Jocelyn Crane will be overwhelm-
ingly grateful that Smith recognized her individualized
needs and turned her loose in the midst of truly wonderful opportunities for preparing for the life she wanted.
Not just one teacher but a number of them urged and
helped her to get the best Smith could give her, and as
much of it as she could assimilate. For her last two years
she took everything the college offered that pertained
directly or indirectly to a zoologist's life—courses in com-
parative anatomy, paleontology, anthropology, entomol-
ogy, and embryology. As a candidate for special honors,
excused from examinations till the end of her senior
year, she had weekly conferences with professors, special
laboratory work in addition to that done by students not

aiming at honors, and prepared a thesis based on her own original research. For Jocelyn Crane, Smith was an embryo zoologist's "all this and heaven, too." She was permitted to attend English, art, and other cultural lecture courses as free time allowed, absorbing what could be absorbed in this way. In 1930 she was graduated with Phi Beta Kappa and highest honors, with an A.B. in zoology, and left immediately for New York City and a job at the Tropical Research Department of the New York Zoological Society, which has been her mailing address ever since.

The man who gave her the job was William Beebe. Like numerous young zoology majors of that day she wanted to work with this colorful, adventuresome scientist, and a friend of her mother's had arranged for Jocelyn to meet him and Mrs. Beebe socially, at a lunch during Christmas vacation of her junior year. Thirty years her senior and with long experience in selecting young scientists, Dr. Beebe was not an easy man to convince. "I had to work like blazes for eighteen months," she recalls, "through letters, three additional interviews, a deluge of good marks, copies of term papers and my entire honors thesis to convince him it was worthwhile to give me a trial as a volunteer worker."

The result of her efforts was that she scarcely had time to catch up on sleep after commencement before she found herself at the Zoological Society's Research Laboratories at Nonsuch Island, Bermuda, where Dr. Beebe had recently begun to use the bathysphere to explore the ocean's depths and extend his studies of the strange creatures that live "down under."

Fishes were not Miss Crane's first love, but they were something she would see a lot of in the next dozen years, as William Beebe continued his studies of deep-sea varieties in the vicinity of Bermuda. She would accompany him, as a research biologist, to this spot some six or eight times in the next decade. On each of these expeditions the group spent months at a time at their Bermuda field station, going out daily on a boat of some kind that could be moved over the radius of ocean whose depths were to be explored visually by bathysphere, and collecting specimens in nets. Fish took on new interests for Jocelyn Crane as she studied the externals and internals of what came up in the nets, and life provided an entirely new kind of thrill when she was invited to climb into the 54-inch steel globe, fit herself into the space available for a second passenger, and begin the descent through greenish water, past the submerged hull of the boat from which they had been hoisted.

With eyes glued to a window past which small living creatures swam, she watched the color of the water change to bluish-green and then a darkening blue. Little flashes of light appeared as the darkness changed to a deeper blue, the luminescence of sea life that had perpetuated itself for millions of years without light or air. Now came the fun—if you can enjoy yourself in such a situation—of watching colorful animals, some of them truly grotesque, as Beebe threw strong beams of light into the darkness. More amazing, even, than what she saw was what she heard as Beebe flashed his lightning-like observations through the bathysphere's telephone to the scientist listening and recording above. His quick recognition of what he saw gave Jocelyn Crane an increased respect for her director's speed and keenness of observation. It would have taken her much longer to recognize what he recognized in a flash—and what she already knew enough about to know he was right as soon as he spoke it.

Dr. Beebe himself went down more than 3000 feet one day in 1934, but the farthest he took Miss Crane was almost a quarter of a mile. Though it may have been fun for a person who has no fear of being within a hollow steel sphere suspended on steel cables as it is submitted to the terrific water pressures of a quarter of a mile down, it was hard work to make the reports that followed these descents and the other work going on at the station. Anyone who sees the long technical papers that give to the world the knowledge derived from such studies and observations recognizes the long months of meticulously careful dissections and analyses, the scientific knowledge, the keenness of observation, and the sheer mental and physical drudgery that goes into such reports.

Jocelyn Crane's name is signed with William Beebe's to four such detailed reports on deep sea fishes of these Bermuda expeditions. They describe in minute detail many hundreds of specimens, classify them into scores of species, and give them their proper place among the data accumulated over the years by scientists who have classified thousands of other specimens of the same, and other, species.

With each passing year Miss Crane knew more and more definitely that living creatures interested her more than dead creatures. She could dissect and analyze a dead specimen with the best of her fellow zoologists and attain a certain satisfaction in adding to man's knowledge of life in that way. But the behavior of small animals while they were alive was the interest that motivated her most urgently. Also, she had begun to observe crabs, and discovered how much their behavior patterns interested her. She wanted to make studies of these creatures because, watching them at work and in their relationships with each other, she felt sure the things they were doing might help reveal secrets still hidden from human minds. The social habits of small animals became her main interest now, not so much by decision as by her natural arrival at a vision of the goal toward which she had been born to work.

So now she faced a decision any young zoologist on her way up must make. Should she take her Ph.D. or go ahead in this fascinating field of small-animal behavior without it? Though she made her decision against a doctorate, it is not one she recommends to other young women. Let her explain it in her own words:

"I thought about it and talked it over with Dr. Beebe. I knew definitely I would never want to teach and that I did want to study the behavior of small animals in their natural habitations. Practically everything I could do in a university laboratory I had already done and could go on doing at the zoo laboratory. Dr. Beebe and I both believed I had taken at Smith all the academic work I needed for the type of zoological studies I wanted to make, so I decided against going back to college.

"It has worked out well for me because I have been able to stay on with the Society and Dr. Beebe, do the work I wanted to do, and advance to administrative duties in our Department of Tropical Research. If I had suddenly needed to find a new job ten or fifteen years after college, my lack of a Ph.D. might have counted heavily against my getting the best opportunity. I took that risk and I am glad I took it. But I honestly could not advise others to take it. I was lucky!"

Lucky—yes—for five years after her graduation she was able to take her first trip to Asia. In a village in Kurdistan where she established herself for a few months in order to study insects living in its mountainous surroundings, a small boy reached inside his scarlet jacket one day and brought out just what she had been wanting—a squirming gray-furred baby squirrel fresh from a nest in a plane tree where very recently it had been born. Too young to have had opportunity to watch how squirrels behave who have to fend for themselves, Miss Crane wanted to see how it would act if taken from its natural habitat, fed and cared for without effort on its part, and brought up indoors as a pet.

Disaster to this experiment seemed to have occurred three days later when, frightened by a combination of circumstances in the room where she sat typing, the baby squirrel ran straight into her blazing fireplace. It came out quickly, ran whimpering up her stone wall and hid in a hole in a rafter. Not until its suppertime was she able to coax it down again, with a medicine dropper full of goat's milk. Its fur was singed, its whiskers burned off to a stubble, but to her great joy it was not truly harmed. She named it Shadrach* and made a soft ribbon harness for it so she could put it on a leash and watch its actions out

* *See* Daniel 3:13-26.

of doors. She soon learned she could tell when a dog or strange human being was approaching because Shadrach promptly climbed up and hid in her pocket.

Yet he did not fear all animals—at least not when he met them indoors. One evening while she was typing, she heard a noise and saw two large-eyed wild rats squeezing through a crack in her door. When they and the ends of their plumed tails were safely inside, they sat up, sniffed, and cautiously made their way toward some walnut crumbs left over from Shadrach's supper, beside which he was sleeping in his hollow gourd. He wakened, stuck first his nose, then his whole head, out of the gourd and eyed the rats. They retreated momentarily. Then Shadrach grunted and went back to sleep. The rats finished his supper, departed, and returned for repeat performances the next evening and most evenings thereafter till Miss Crane and Shadrach departed for America. Apparently he was not only unafraid of the rats but willing to share with them the food for which he had never worked. Nevertheless, the day after the rats' first visit Miss Crane saw Shadrach, for the first time, go through all the motions of digging a hole in her floor, carrying an actual nut to the make-believe hole and burying it—as though some instinct about the possibility of someday needing food had been wakened by the experience.

Following her studies in Kurdistan, the Tropical Research Department's field station for two years was on a yacht moving about in the Gulf of California and eastern Pacific Ocean, where Miss Crane studied crabs. Her first of many published papers on these animals described those found on trips along the coast of the lower California peninsula and west coasts of Mexico and Central America. Putting in at shore collecting stations all along the way, she made collections of brachyuran crabs to take back to New York for study. But first of all she studied them alive. Their colors, ranging from brilliant coral red to dark brown, with yellow and yellow-green marbling, were one of their interesting aspects. The carapace (outer shell) of one female that gave her a long chase over the sand on a gray stormy day was a violet-gray when captured. After it had sat in a sandy-bottomed box in the sun for a couple of days, it was a moderately brilliant coral. She found, as is true in some other species of animal life, that the adult male crabs were brightest in color, the females paler, and the youngsters palest of all.

She watched literally hundreds of crabs dig their burrows, and found that they constructed them in three distinct architectural patterns. She noted that these habits needed further study, as did the way the crabs varied in methods of carrying their sand loads and stamping down the sand to make their homes as they wanted them. She watched the crabs as they appeared at the doors of their burrows promptly as the high tide began to recede. Resting for a few moments first, they then cleaned themselves thoroughly, beginning with "polishing their eyes with the palp of the third maxilliped." After an hour had passed, the crabs, beginning usually with the largest, started toward the edge of the tide to feed on what had been washed up for them, leaving what had been deposited near their burrows until later. Walking slowly at first, then more rapidly, the animals finally reached a racing gait.

Before time for the tide to advance again, back they came to their burrows to repair old or build new ones, feeding at whatever had been left at their front doors as they worked. "Then the crabs gradually returned to their burrows, usually pulling in a plug of sand after them. Fifty minutes before high tide not a crab would be left on the beach." High tide, low tide—and the story was repeated day after day.

This was only the beginning of her voluminous work on these seashore creatures that are found all over the world. And she can make crabs, especially fiddler crabs, so interesting that most people who hear her talk or see her slides and motion pictures of them stop wondering why she has spent so many months of so many years sitting on mudbanks studying their behavior and wants to continue the habit. Crabs to her are not something to look for on the menu card but one of a group of three little animals (spiders and butterflies are the others) whose social behavior has enough variety and complexity to interest her always. She became an expert motion picture camera operator in color as well as in black and white because motion pictures in color are an asset for best study of animals whose coloration seems to have a great deal to do with their social life, as it has with all three of her favorite groups.

As is apparent from all this, the first dozen years of Miss Crane's work life had not given her contact with the tropical jungles she had dreamed of visiting, as a child, but that lack was not to be permanent. In 1942 it became possible for the Tropical Research Department to establish a temporary field station near Caripito,

Venezuela, through the interest of American oil companies operating in that vicinity. The work accomplished that year was so successful that the financing of a permanent station in the jungles of South America was made possible. To Miss Crane now fell the task and opportunity to explore parts of Venezuela, Colombia, and Ecuador to find the best location for the station.

A job of this kind is not without physical hardships. Nor is it easy to determine which site is neither too wet nor too dry, which is accessible enough to the outside world for incoming supplies not to be too difficult a problem, which has the best variety of animal and plant life that would continue for some time to be undisturbed by human beings and—as it turned out unexpectedly— which would not be too near Motilone Indians, who took pleasure in killing white people. Getting off a plane, she would get into a saddle and spend days on horseback exploring jungles, studying signs that might tell her whether abundant rainfall in a jungle would leave it soaked and flooded for months at a time and thus inhabitable for fewer creatures, or whether a better-distributed rainfall in another jungle might be on a slope whose soil dried off so rapidly that its wild life would be dormant when it was most wanted for study.

Other days were spent on lakes and rivers studying their jungle-lined shores and banks. Though she was free of the kind of fears that afflict many people, she confessed later that, when her pilot called her attention one day to a jungle over which they were flying and mentioned the murderous tribe into whose hands they would fall in case of accident, "A month before, that remark

would have sounded like a joke, but now, half unconsciously, my ears began to take unashamed interest in the
regularity of the motor's roar."

Out of that trip came decisions that resulted in the
Zoological Society's new field station, Rancho Grande, on
a mountaintop in northern Venezuela, where Miss Crane
was soon deep in studies of jumping spiders. She found
the courting habits of these puzzling creatures had points
of similarity to those of the fiddler crab. Like the American fiddler, who performs long and intricate dances as
he waves his longer claw in wooing his mate, these spiders,
too, performed dances in attracting their mates. Males
fought rival males in "battles as complex and stylized as
the duels of Javanese dancers," and survivors wooed
mates as the color of their eyes changed from green to
black and back to green again at a frantic rate of speed.
Her papers on the courting habits of these spiders are
recognized as of the same high value among studies of
animal behavior as are her papers on crabs.

In the Andes, and later in Trinidad, she studied butterflies, too. One of the things about which she has long
been curious is the brilliant coloring of some of the small
animals of the tropics. Is this coloring ever of use in their
social relationships? Miss Crane does not know the full
answer but some of her work with butterflies has given a
partial one. She put them under a mild anesthetic, gently
scraped off the dustlike flakes that give them color, and
painted them any color she wanted. She could make a
complete wallflower out of a once-attractive female by
painting her wings black, and attract both males and
females to orange-red pseudo-butterflies made of out of

felt. So color does, sometimes at least, help attract mates and perpetuate the species.

Not until World War II was well over was Miss Crane able to get back to Asia, visit the South Pacific and then Africa. Early in the 1950's the National Science Foundation gave her a grant making it possible, with the Zoological Society's co-operation, for her to spend a third of her time each year for five years making a world-wide study of Ocypodid crabs. Such funds are not given lightly, but this group of crustaceans is particularly suitable for the type of behavior studies Miss Crane wanted to make of it because its evolutionary aspects happen to make it of interest not only to zoologists but to other biologists as well. Her work made possible by this grant will, therefore, have value for other specialists in the general field of biology.

For three successive years she set off, all alone, for those parts of the world she had so long wanted to visit, with camera equipment and other necessary paraphernalia, and could soon be found sitting on mudflats in Malaya, on Tahiti and other South Sea islands, and in Africa. The results of this extended study of a cosmopolitan small animal group promises to be, when completed and published, the most authoritative, colorful, and complete scientific contribution ever made on this subject. Nor will its interest be limited to scientists. Laymen, too, are eager for knowledge that reveals similarities and differences in manifestations of life, wherever they are found. The unity of the life force, the evolution of man and of animals, the revelation of their deep ancestral roots, are subjects that intrigue the minds of many thinking human beings. Already some of Miss Crane's discoveries in the realm of animal behavior have widened man's knowledge and stretched his imagination in this field.

In one of his books ex-Harvard President James Conant says that for most scientists "the justification of their work is to be found in the sheer joy of its creativeness." He likens the spirit which moves them to the "imaginative vision which inspires an artist." Jocelyn Crane is, beyond question, such a scientist. She works primarily for the sheer joy of doing what she does, and in no way has this lessened the respect in which her work is held by her peers. She believes that studies of the behavior of living animals offer valuable clues to and information about the evolution of the whole animal species, and that zoologists will be able to contribute further to this subject by wise selection for new studies.

To help gather this information is her aim. Frankly, though, it is not the main driving force behind her work. She has a deep-seated need of know more about small living creatures, and she labors primarily to satisfy her own thirst for this kind of knowledge. Young enough to have the possibility of much good work ahead of her, she is likely to keep on doing the things that can ease but not quench that thirst.

FLORENCE VAN STRATEN

(1913–   )

●●●

Who joined the Waves in World War II, was assigned
to meteorological work, and has helped responsibly in
developing our modern Naval Weather Service

M ETEOROLOGY is a young science. Except for weather
forecasting, which had advanced somewhat after teleg-
raphy came into use, it had scarcely begun to develop
before the outbreak of World War II. Florence van
Straten (pronounced Stratton) was thrust into this infant
science by her superior officers when she joined the Waves
after the United States had entered the war. She has
been in it ever since, first as a U.S. naval officer and, since
1946, as a civilian technical adviser in the Office of the
Chief of Naval Operations. In these capacities she has
been a responsible factor in some of the significant
achievements that are advancing this still young science
step by step toward its goal.

Meteorology's goal, incidentally, goes far beyond the

124

usual meaning attached to the *meteor* in its name. Its aim is complete understanding of all the physical processes which combine to produce "the weather," whether by that word we mean a typhoon in the Pacific, a drought in India or Texas, or behavior patterns in the upper atmosphere encountered by airplanes or earth satellites. In short, meteorology is the science of the atmosphere.

One of the assets Florence van Straten brought to work in this young science when she joined the U.S. Naval Reserve was a Ph.D. in physical chemistry. Within five weeks it had assured her a place in the first group of twenty-five Waves selected for training in aerological engineering (the Navy term for meteorology) to see if women could be used successfully to overcome the shortage of available men meteorologists. Ensign van Straten was one of the twenty-two who survived the stiff nine-month course laid out for this group at the Massachusetts Institute of Technology, with marks that warranted diplomas as Certificated Meteorologists. The caliber of intellectual discipline inherent in this course may be judged by the fact that, had she not already had her Ph.D., her nine months of work would have been accepted as two and a half years of graduate credit toward a Ph.D. in aerological engineering at M.I.T. The three college-graduate Waves who flunked the course are certainly not to be branded as having had low IQ's!

Yet Florence van Straten's capacities for mastery of the physical sciences were something she had never planned to cultivate until she was ready for her last semester's work in high school. She had grown up knowing definitely what she wanted to do with her life, and it had nothing to do with science. She was going to be a writer. Hers was a good home to provide a helpful background for a young writer's development. Her parents, immigrants from Holland, consisted of a mother who was a brilliant linguist in six languages (and the highest salaried woman in Holland when she was married by proxy to Jacques van Straten and left on the next boat to join him in New York) and a father who wanted to help his only child prepare for whatever kind of work she preferred.

His work as financial representative for Metro-Goldwyn-Mayer Pictures, with headquarters in New York City, took him abroad occasionally and gave Florence an opportunity to spend one year of her secondary school life in Nice, where she improved her French. (She always spoke English and Dutch with equal fluency.) All this plus enough German, Italian, and Spanish from her parents, so that "I haven't needed to go hungry in any of these languages ever since," was excellent cultural background for an embryo writer. So Florence moved along in her schooling not much impressed one way or another by the fact that, though English was her favorite study, she liked her other studies, too, and made equally good marks in all of them. It was more or less accepted by the three van Stratens that Florence was going to be a writer.

But writing, all three knew, is not a profession you decide to enter, go to college to prepare for, and emerge ready to make a living at. One of the riddles her father used to ask her to remind her of that was, "Why do writers live in garrets?" She knew the answer: "Because they can't live on the first two or three stories." The knowledge that writers do not usually make enough money to live on till they are older had especial significance for Florence because she would graduate from Girls High School in Brooklyn when barely sixteen. Tutoring from her mother and a natural aptitude for making straight A's had shortened her schooling by two years.

Added to this, Jacques van Straten, always a strong influence in his daughter's life, had had an experience as a youth in Amsterdam that had taught him life does not always turn out the way a person plans it. With every intention of becoming a doctor he was just beginning college work when his well-to-do family was suddenly left penniless and he had to shoulder the family's financial responsibilities with no preparation for it. With this experience in mind he suggested to his daughter, "Why not use some of your time in college to prepare yourself to make a living in some field of work other than writing—just in case you ever need to?"

The idea was so reasonable that Florence readily accepted it. The trouble was, she had no idea what a second choice of work would be. Mr. van Straten thought, then, it would be a good idea to ask her high-school principal for a suggestion, and did so. After some thought her principal suggested chemistry—one of the few subjects Florence had never studied. She still had one semester's high-school work ahead of her, so she signed up for a course in chemistry and, "I liked it as I always liked what I studied; so if Dad and my high-school principal thought it was a field in which I could always earn a living, it satisfied me, too."

As casually as this the decision was made that caused

an unsuspecting embryo scientist to register at New York University with English and chemistry as her two majors, and the privilege of taking her bachelor's degree in either subject. She never dreamed that degree would be other than in English.

As she was beginning her last year in college an event beyond her control happened that was soon to change the direction in which she was going as unexpectedly as the course of her father's life had been changed. A faculty member became ill and Florence was asked to take one of his freshman laboratory classes in chemistry till he recovered. He did not recover, and she taught the class throughout the year. Spring came, and with it the offer of a teaching fellowship for the following year, with one proviso—a big one in her case. To be eligible for the fellowship she would have to accept her bachelor's degree in chemistry instead of English, and use the fellowship for study toward a Ph.D. in chemistry.

She thought it over well. She was only nineteen. (High school and college had each taken only three and a half years.) All experience was grist for the writer. She accepted, took her B.S. in chemistry *cum laude* in 1933 and was elected to Phi Beta Kappa.

It was during this period that Florence van Straten, who had been writing fiction all through high school and college, discovered she was completely unable to write. So imbued had she become with the scientist's ideal of truth and his scientific approach to it that she found herself asking herself how she could ever want to write fiction again. A young woman of high ideals herself, truth was of importance to her. So greatly had her contact with science influenced her, the scientific approach had unconsciously become to her the only sincere approach to truth. Within a few years, however, she had matured to the place where she understood, to put it into her own words, that "the serious fiction writer and scientist each seeks truth in his own way. Though I am primarily a scientist, I believe art is another way of searching for the universal truth the scientist is trying to express. Truth must be a unified whole, not little compartmented sections labeled 'scientific truth,' 'religious truth,' 'artistic truth.' "

As this gradually became clearer to her, she found herself beginning to write again. In this she follows the pattern of many other distinguished scientists who develop and retain a deep personal interest in one of the arts and find it wise, maybe even necessary, to keep this interest alive, though not at a professional level. Einstein with his violin playing was one of many examples of scientists whose lifelong hobby lay in pursuit of an art. Gerty Cori had to read all her life, and feed her interest in art constantly.

Not until after she had her diploma as a Certificated Meteorologist did Dr. van Straten find the scientific focus that was to become a long-time challenge to and direction-finder for her mind. She had remained at New York University, a lesser member of its faculty, for nine years after she had her B.S., taking her Ph.D. in physical chemistry along the way. Results of several researches made in collaboration with William F. Ehret had achieved publication in scientific journals and pursuit of an exact science had had its satisfactions. But the highly specialized study at M.I.T. had shown her that a field like meteorology, in the throes of its transformation from art to science, offered challenging opportunities.

Maybe the force of the challenge was accentuated because she was plunged into this experience at a time when our Navy was fighting for its life—and ours—in a war on two oceans. Especially in the Pacific there was need of greater knowledge of weather conditions, and of how to use available knowledge in the best way. Traditionally, weather has had a great deal to do with the results of naval engagements. Any schoolchild knows that an unforeseen change in the wind favorable to the British fleet gave advantage to the Spanish Armada instead and enabled it to escape. Our Naval Weather Service's job in World War II was to see to it that our ships did not, as far as could be avoided, meet weather conditions accidentally, and that, as far as possible, weather conditions would be foreseen and used to advantage in winning battles. The job was all the more difficult because, in the Pacific, the Japanese might quite naturally be expected to know more about weather conditions than the United States and her allies.

Dr. van Straten obviously would not be one of those who, in planes or ships, gathered and transmitted weather information. That work does not take Ph.D.'s in science. Her job would be to apply scientific knowledge in developing new methods and techniques that would, as one example, enable aerological officers on board naval vessels to advise commanding officers daily—even hourly—as to weather conditions, as far ahead as possible. To give a single instance of what was needed:

In the launching and recovery of planes from an aircraft carrier deck, the ship must head into the wind and the combined speed of wind and ship must exceed a certain minimum. The trick is to find suitable winds (as close to the target as possible) for launching, to keep the ships at safe range during the air strike, and to have returning planes and ships rendezvous again in another favorable wind situation. The aerological officer must contribute accurate information if the carrier air strike is to be well executed.

Many weather facts from distant areas were essential for the types of forecasting needed during World War II. Radar techniques were developed that identified distinctive radar echoes with various types of weather conditions. For example, one of the means used to insure adequate winds across the carrier deck was to hunt a thunderstorm on a radar scope, steam to it, then circle the area on its fringes. Higher winds associated with the thunderstorm permitted take-off or recovery of planes in a region otherwise beset my calms.

In one of the air attacks on the Marshall and Gilbert islands Japanese bombers found the task force just as the last planes were being landed back on it. Since planes have a far greater speed than ships, the problem was to get the task force away from the bombers if possible. The aerological officer found the answer. He identified and determined the position of a cold front some distance away that would offer a natural smoke screen. The task force headed for the latitude and longitude he recommended, made it safely, and then adjusted the speed of the ships to that of the cold front. Japanese planes hunting for them were audible. After a good many hours, when evidence showed the planes had given up, the task force steamed safely back to Pearl Harbor.

Instances like this are a greater meteorological achievement than most laymen realize. Forecasting weather conditions on or near the earth's surface is much more difficult than forecasting conditions higher in the atmosphere. Laymen find it easy to laugh when the weatherman's prediction is wrong, but Dr. van Straten maintains this happens less often than we think. "It's just that everyone remembers the 'busts' and forgets the 'hits.'" The meteorologist knows it is easier to predict accurately the atmospheric conditions a plane will meet in flying from New York to Los Angeles than to predict conditions at either of these cities. Conditions near the earth's surface are more erratic because of all the local effects of terrain. To be really accurate in forecasting for a twenty-four to thirty-six hour period, he must have all necessary data. But all necessary data are not available to him.

A heartbreaking incident occurred in the early days of Dr. van Straten's naval service, showing what the absence of essential data can do. In our step-by-step occupation of Pacific Islands aerological officers selected the time for each landing. In the great majority of cases the weather turned out favorable for the operation. In one case serious loss of life and equipment occurred because unpredicted turbulent conditions arose in the ocean during the landing. They were due, it could be determined later, to a typhoon that had occurred a thousand miles from the island, in a spot in the Pacific where no plane or automatic weather station had caught it.

By the time the war was over Florence van Straten's

mind had been truly challenged by the vast amount of
the unknown in atmospheric conditions that needed to
become known. Her superior officers in the Naval
Weather Service had been impressed by the fact that she
had what was needed for their work. Comparatively few
scientists were available who were as well equipped as
she was for developing knowledge of atmospheric conditions into usable scientific procedures. That she preferred to continue her work as a civilian was no drawback,
since she could readily be transferred from the active to
the inactive Naval Reserve list. So, exchanging her uniform with lieutenant commander leaves for civilian
clothes in 1946, she became a civilian advisor for the
Naval Weather Service, which she has been ever since.
And, as the years passed, "I became a sort of trouble-
shooter for the Navy," on problems ranging all the way
from fogs to radioactive fallouts.

It would be her creativity as a trouble-shooter that
would earn for her the Navy's Meritorious Civilian Service Award after ten years of civilian service—during
which, incidentally, she attained rank as commander in
the Naval Reserve. But one of the first big assignments
when the war was over was not a trouble-shooting job at
all. It came about because many scientists working on
long-range missiles designed to enter the upper atmosphere were seemingly unaware of their need for aid from
meteorologists. They were forgetting that atmospheric
conditions—wind, temperature, density—would affect the
characteristics of their "birds." The Naval Weather Service, on the other hand, believed an analysis of the upper
atmosphere and its variations would reveal factors that

should be taken into account in the design of long-range missiles. In this belief they decided to obtain and analyze information on normal and abnormal wind and temperature conditions to an altitude of 100,000 feet. Then came the announcement that the project established to prepare and analyze the data would be under the direction of Dr. F. W. van Straten.

It was a long-term sizable undertaking, as any one who glances through the four thick technical reports that eventually emerged from Dr. van Straten's office must recognize. Again, her job was not to take the observations but to direct the project of analyzing thousands of observations made in many different ways, on the foundation of her knowledge of the science inherent in such a study. Data from a score of geographical locations ranging from Greenland to Japan came to her desk. The results of her analyses, in text, table, and graphic form, were presented piecemeal, over a period of two years, for immediate use by scientists.

These graphs and tables made missile people aware of their need for help from meteorologists. The pleasant theory held by some—that when a missile entered the stratosphere (30,000 to 40,000 feet above the earth), it entered a placid, storm-free area—was shattered. Some of the earliest observations showed that balloons capable of reaching 100,000 feet with a 70-pound weight suspended from them oscillated violently in the stratosphere. One set of observations showed winds strong enough at 65,000 to 70,000 feet to thrust a 55-pound weight upward so violently that it ripped the bag of the balloon. Any missile that had to enter the stratosphere needed either to avoid these winds or be prepared to enter them without disaster.

Techniques for using balloons in gathering wind and weather information have improved since those studies were made, and Dr. van Straten has been one of the scientists responsible for this. By the middle of the 1950's our Navy was launching 40-foot balloons daily in Japan, balloons whose bags were the thickness of a cellophane wrapper on a package of cigarettes, yet which carried more than 600 pounds of radio and other equipment and ballast. Launched by the insertion of a bubble of helium into the bag, they rise to 30,000 feet, level off, and float at that height, radioing at two-hour periods their position, temperature, and air pressure. Traveling with the winds, they cross the Pacific Ocean, pass over the United States, then cross the Atlantic Ocean and explode themselves as they approach Europe's shore line to prevent international complications. By checking their position with each radio report, wind speeds are known daily for the whole distance they travel.

Much of Dr. van Straten's work is still secret, as some of the work already described was secret at one time. Parts of the achievement that earned her Meritorious Civilian Service Award in 1956 can be told about without violation of the secrecy that surrounds other aspects of it. As years had passed, she had become one of the scientists called upon to suggest solutions for problems affecting Navy work which no one knew exactly how to attack. Sometimes she came up with an original and effective answer. She might suggest having a new piece of equipment designed, or work out a new technique using existing means, or show that if new data were gathered the problem could be solved. Her ideas were not always used—for example, a sonic device that would prevent formation of ice on airplanes was not developed, though the idea won a patent for her. On the other hand, a radar-facsimile system which automatically plots out scope information at the radar set or, simultaneously, at any number of air stations is being developed.

One result of her proven ability to solve new problems was that she was given considerable freedom to work on unassigned problems if she herself recognized their importance. In this way she began to study certain aspects of the problems of radioactive fallout, especially the problem of trying to ensure our country's survival in case of atomic attack. Sitting at her desk in Washington in the Office of the Chief of Naval Operations, she found herself thinking:

"Suppose Washington were bombed. How could authorities know the best steps to take to save lives and move hospitals and still uncontaminated supplies to the safest possible spot?"

Radioactive particles, she knew, follow definite fallout patterns that are influenced by atmospheric conditions. They are extremely intense in some zones and very much less intense in others, even those nearer the site of the explosion. They vary with the passing of time. Putting her mind to the task, she formulated a scientific procedure for computing radioactive fallout and patterns under any atmospheric conditions. This kind of information, if determined daily, would enable authorities in any locality to know immediately how to evacuate a bombed zone with greatest security for all concerned.

It was not a particularly expensive or difficult precautionary measure to put into effect, yet, as often happens with a new idea, no one in authority was sufficiently interested to take it up. A question existed in many minds as to whether radioactive fallout would prove to be a significant hazard or not. So Dr. van Straten put her plan away among her papers and turned to other matters. Then, a year or so later, the story burst upon the world that Japanese fishermen had suffered serious injury from radioactive fallouts following one of our atomic tests in the Pacific. Immediately people all over the world were aroused and our government sent out an order to all our Armed Services to "take account of radioactive fallouts" in everything they did. Unfortunately, no one knew how to "take account."

One person, at least, though, had a good idea. Florence van Straten dusted off her papers containing the basic know-how for solving this problem, made revisions wherever newer knowledge obtained from more recent tests dictated revision, and presented her plans again. They proved to be what was needed for "taking account."

The citation on the Meritorious Civilian Award she received for this work mentions her initiative. She had recognized and solved the problem without being asked —or told—to solve it. As a result of her work an aerological officer at every Naval Station, on sea or land, now plots a daily graph that identifies the pattern radioactive fallout would follow that day if a bomb were exploded in his area. It is part of his daily work to ascertain, under existing atmospheric conditions, the best direction for ships to take without passing through zones of heaviest fallout concentration or, if he is based on land, the safest direction and location in which hospitals, food, and medical supplies and population should be evacuated.

Dr. van Straten's work has become broader than the confines usually assigned to meteorology. That it is so recognized was made evident early in 1958 when she was named "Woman of the Year" by the Women's Wing of the Aero Medical Association for achievements in and contributions to atmospheric physics. She believes that meteorology itself, however, offers an interesting field and sufficient opportunity to attract more young women than have yet shown much desire to enter it. (Estimates in the middle 1950's were that only about 2 per cent of all meteorologists with professional standing were women.) Though weather forecasting is the best known activity in meteorology, she believes research and other forms of laboratory work, and teaching, probably offer more attractive opportunities for women than weather forecasting. Climatology's increasing importance to industry is making it a field of growing opportunity. Hydrology, which predicts run-off in rainstorms, is also growing in importance as flood-control work is increasingly undertaken.

Whatever the branch of meteorology one works in, mathematics and the physical sciences are basic requirements—basic, first of all, for enrollment in a college curriculum that gives a bachelor's degree in meteorology. Ph.D.'s are still not too frequent among meteorologists, though they are essential for work such as Dr. van Straten has been able to do. Certainly hers is a scientific field whose future promises more than its past has yet accomplished. Weather making and control of outer space are no longer subjects only for science-fiction writers. They are problems of serious scientific study and in their solution meteorologists are going to have a share.

GLADYS ANDERSON EMERSON

(1903–   )

●◦●

Biochemist whose researches with experimental animals
have increased our knowledge of the effects of vitamin
deficiencies on the human body

Nothing in Gladys Emerson's early life indicated what
her future was going to be, unless it was a happy disposi-
tion that would help ease the way for her no matter what
field of life or work she chose. Down in Texas, where her
parents had moved when she was still a baby from the
small town in Caldwell, Kansas, where she had been born,
she grew into her teens without a brother, a sister, or any
desire or need to keep her nose pressed uncomfortably
close against an educational grindstone. Learning from
books and teachers came easily enough for her to have
plenty of good times without endangering her scholastic
standing. She started early to find time to get fun out of
life and, though her ideas of what constituted a good
time matured as she grew older, she never found a reason

to change that early pattern of alternating work and play. When, in 1956, she settled into a completely new environment to take over a new kind of job—chairman of the Department of Home Economics of the University of California on its Los Angeles campus—she took with her a piano, three or four cameras, a collection of music albums filled mainly with classical records, and the feeling that she hoped she might find a new dog to take the place —if possible—of the beloved wire-hair terrier who, full of years, had recently gone on to his reward.

Like many other schoolgirls Gladys Anderson, as her name was then, was interested in most of the subjects she studied and had no outstanding favorites. In Fort Worth grade schools she found she shared her mother's flair for mathematics as well as her father's interest in history. In the high school at El Reno, Oklahoma, where the family had moved, she discovered she liked Latin and chemistry as much as she liked mathematics, history, and the social sciences. At times it seemed as if she enjoyed public speaking best of all, especially when she captained the debating team that won the state championship. The theater, she found herself daydreaming, might offer what she wanted, or the lecture platform. Whatever her talents appeared to be during high-school days, it is certain none of her teachers would have dared suggest that here was a young woman who would be honored by her peers for scientific achievement before she was fifty.

The stage star phase did not outlast her freshman year at Oklahoma College for Women. That was the year the college dramatic association decided to produce *As You Like It,* and Gladys's dreams soared right off into the clouds picturing herself as Rosalind. When tryouts were over she found herself cast as William, described by Shakespeare as a rustic oaf in love with Audrey, a country wench. She played the part but a fatal blow had been dealt to her stage aspirations. Now only the lecture platform remained.

In all truth, if chemistry had not caught Gladys Anderson's interest as it did, it is more than likely that she could have made good as a lecturer. Ever since she began to make a name for herself as a scientist, she has been in demand as a public speaker. Mount Holyoke, Wilson, Wells, Barnard, and other women's colleges have invited her to their platforms. Yale, Harvard, Brown, the University of Pennsylvania and other universities, Rensselaer Polytechnic Institute and the Medical School of the University of California have had her lecture or conduct seminars for their students. Rotary, Kiwanis and other clubs have sought her out. All this has been in addition to her appearances before scientific gatherings where, as might naturally be expected, she frequently speaks or reads a paper.

Throughout her undergraduate college years, as in high-school days, she continued to play no academic favorites because she had found no single study that appealed to her more than did a number of others. At Oklahoma College for Women she took two baccalaureates in her stride—a B.S. in physics and chemistry and an A.B. in history and English. As president of student government she had practice once a week in developing platform presence. Though she was never one of the college's star athletes, a game of tennis now and then helped keep a figure in trim that was going to bear a little watching all her life. Busy as she was with college activities and as a teaching assistant in chemistry and physics for two years, she found time for piano practice and missed very little of the fun students in Chickasha made for themselves.

She had had her choice, at OCW, of becoming an assistant in either the science or history departments and had chosen science. For her first year of graduate work she reversed that decision. She went to Stanford University, served there as a teaching assistant, and received her Master's degree in history the following spring. The next year found her head of the department in social sciences in a junior high school in Oklahoma City.

Then, at the age of twenty-three, she took the step that set Gladys Anderson on the path that would lead to the Garvan Medal for distinguished work in chemistry twenty-six years later. Two attractive teaching opportunities offered themselves, one in the arts and the other in the sciences. The latter was a Fellowship in Nutrition at the University of California in Berkeley. Faced with opportunity for graduate study and with immediate need to decide between the social sciences and biochemistry, she chose the fellowship that offered advance work in science.

By the end of that year's work at Berkeley her interest in biochemistry had become permanently focused. After three years of teaching at the University of California, and one at Iowa State College earning money of her own, she returned to the University of California and took her Ph.D. in animal nutrition and biochemistry in 1932. Somewhere along the way she changed her name, as many young women scientists do, to that of a fellow scientist.

One recognized weak spot in her education as a bio-chemist was an inability to read German with ease, or to speak it conversationally. Much of the scientific work with which she would want to keep up would be published first in German, and scientific meetings are often so international in character that facility with the German language as it is spoken would also be an asset. Moreover, young Dr. Emerson believed living in a foreign country, as well as contact with and studying under distinguished German scientists, would be a developing experience for her. So she decided upon a year's study abroad and selected Göttingen University, where Adolph Windaus was professor of chemistry and director of the university laboratories. Windaus had been the recipient of the Nobel Prize in chemistry a few years earlier for his researches in sterols—a group of molecular alcohols in which cholesterol is most widely known to the layman—especially in their relation to vitamins, in which Dr. Emerson was already interested.

That year at Göttingen turned out to be not as pleasant an experience as she had hoped for. The Nazis took control of Germany six months after Gladys Emerson arrived there. People soon began to disappear from universities, and Göttingen was no exception. Professor Windaus was not affected by racial decrees, and Dr. Emerson was able to work with him and other outstanding faculty members and graduate students. One of them, Adolph Butenandt, was launching out on his work on the body chemicals called hormones that would bring him the Nobel Prize a few years later—an honor he would be forced to decline because, by Nazi decree, German scientists were not permitted to accept Nobel Prizes at that time. Despite increasingly uncertain conditions Dr. Emerson formed professional friendships that year at Göttingen that she was able to renew after the power of the Nazis had been crushed and many of the Göttingen group became leaders in the reorganization of German universities, science, and industry.

A big disappointment of the year and a half abroad was that living and working in an environment where German was constantly spoken did not develop in her anything that could be called fluency in speaking the German language.

"I can read it easily enough," she says, "and I can manage to carry on a conservation well enough to make myself understood. But it is painful to the ear and I know what it must sound like to a person who knows the language well. Nevertheless, I try my German every time I go to Europe—and my targets invariably answer in perfect English!"

Fortunately, her lack of fluency in conversational German would never stand in her way in trying to establish communication with the experimental animals with which her work was going to be accomplished when she got back home. The spoken word would not be important here, not even when she worked up from white rats and dogs to include vicious, temperamental, and expensive little rhesus monkeys. To the qualified scientists all these animals respond to experimental work with messages that are without words yet are open to interpretation in any language in which the scientist thinks.

Back in the United States that next year Dr. Emerson took over as Research Associate at the University of California's Institute of Experimental Biology in charge of nutrition research. She began—or possibly it would be better to say she continued at a higher level—her work of trying to discover and interpret, through planned experiments in feeding, what animals could reveal about the effects upon human beings of chemical substances in our foods. White rats, hamsters, and dogs would be used because, like man, they are mammals, so named because their females have mammary glands for secreting milk that enables them to suckle their young. White rats were then and still are most frequently used for many types of experimental work not only because they are comparatively inexpensive to breed and care for but because their response to food and drugs has proved to be more similar to man's response than that of most of the lower vertebrates.

The institute to which she was returning late in 1933 was in the midst of research work on vitamin E. Its Director, Herbert M. Evans, had identified and named this vitamin, and it was already spoken of as the "reproductive vitamin" because it had been shown that rats fed on diets that were too low in vitamin E lost their power to reproduce themselves. It seemed, then, as if lack of this vitamin was the cause. If so, might lack of vitamin E be the cause of sterility in human beings? This was a problem calling for further study. That vitamin E existed in grains, vegetables, meat, and milk, and that the germ of the wheat was especially rich in it, were known. The latter fact was particularly interesting in view of the custom in some parts of the world for young married women, especially pregnant women, to eat a handful of wheat kernels every day to insure success in bringing healthy babies into the world. Was this custom, then, rooted in a sound racial instinct or was it merely the expression of an irrational superstition?

Today scientists answer that question in part by telling us the need for vitamin E in human nutrition has not been established. If the wheat kernels actually do help insure successful childbearing, it is probably not because of their vitamin E content. Such statements could not be made, however, until scientists could investigate the functions of this individual vitamin in the absence of other factors. Nature provides it only in intricate combinations with other factors, so it had to be isolated in nature before experimental work satisfactory to the scientist could be undertaken.

Gladys Emerson returned to Berkeley in time to join Dr. Evans and other research workers at the institute in their attempts to isolate vitamin E. Not only did they succeed in doing this, but by 1936 they had isolated it in three different forms, designated as alpha, beta, and gamma tocopherols. Wheat germ oil, corn oil, and cotton seed oils were used as source materials. Then, when studies of the isolated vitamin revealed its structure so that it could be made synthetically in a laboratory, new studies were planned that would enable comparison of the effects of synthetic vitamin E with vitamin E prepared from natural sources. Results of these studies showed the same potency for the natural and synthetic vitamins, and the Berkeley investigators were ready for their studies with experimental animals, hoping that their findings might have some application in medical practice for the benefit of human beings.

Though, as has been said, the value of vitamin E in human reproductive processes is still not known, experimental work soon showed that it actually is a factor essential for the successful reproduction of rats, as had been thought earlier. One study, reported by Dr. Evans and Dr. Emerson in 1939, covered four generations of white rats—nearly 300 animals in all. It showed how fertility decreased in each generation fed on vitamin E-low diets, and how it could be restored in the fourth generation at will by dosages of vitamin E administered to the female rats through stomach tubes.

The following year these same investigators reported on another study in which vitamin E had been administered in the same way. This one showed that muscular dystrophy, which appeared in baby rats suckling from mothers that had been fed a vitamin E-low diet, could be prevented by administration of the vitamin to the mothers beginning the day their litters had been born. The investigators took two litters born on the same day to mothers who had been fed identical vitamin E-low diets, gave half of both litters to each mother to suckle, and administered vitamin E to only one of the mothers. The babies suckled by the vitamin E-dosed mother escaped the muscular dystrophy that afflicted the babies suckled by the vitamin E-low mother, regardless of which mother had borne them.

Making frequent visits to the institute during these years was Mr. George W. Merck, at that time president of Merck and Company, whose laboratories in Rahway, New Jersey, are famous for pharmaceutical products used in our country and many other parts of the world. Connected with this company was the Merck Institute for Therapeutic Research, where experimental work was being carried on, similar to but on a larger scale than that in which Dr. Emerson was engaged at her university-connected institute. Mr. Merck and several of the Merck Institute scientists were familiar with Dr. Emerson's work and personality and had come to the conclusion that she would be a valuable addition to their institute's staff. They convinced her that the opportunities they could offer in New Jersey would make the move worth while. And so it happened in 1942 that, at the age of thirty-nine, Dr. Emerson found herself in New Jersey as head of the Merck Institute's Department of Animal Nutrition, with greater leeway for experimental work financed by a successful pharmaceutical house than is usually possible at a university, where funds are often hard to find.

In making this change Dr. Emerson was entering the industrial world in which so many young women are now employed who want to take up scientific work with no academic preparation beyond baccalaureates in chemistry. With her advanced degrees and years of experience in which she had developed proficiency in scientific research that makes use of experimental animals and shown administrative capacity and ability to get along easily with people in her own and other fields of work—with this to offer she had fitted herself for this greater opportunity.

One facet of her new job would be to help train young women less adequately prepared than she in the techniques of experimental work as she planned and directed researches that would be useful in pharmaceutical and nutritional fields. Trained co-workers were becoming more and more necessary, for our country was already at war and increasing need for women in scientific laboratories was at hand. Scientists themselves were called upon for emergency duties in their laboratories, and part of Dr. Emerson's time would be needed, for the duration, for the Office of Scientific Research and Development. When the war was over, she would be in increasing demand as a lecturer or leader of scientific seminar groups— educational work for which the Merck Institute would want her to have time.

Her early researches at Merck, still accomplished mainly with white rats as experimental animals, centered largely on the B complex family of vitamins. New factors in these truly complex vitamins were being discovered, and as each could be proved of health value in medical practice, it became of commercial value to pharmaceutical houses manufacturing it synthetically. There proved to be at least seven (possibly more) of these vitamins that had originally been thought of simply as vitamin B. Her work in this was similar in many respects to the work she had done earlier, except that different types of diseases were produced by dietaries deficient in whatever specific vitamin, or vitamins, of the B complex were being studied. Rats, hamsters, and sometimes dogs fed foods deficient in these vitamins developed abnormal growth, eye, skin, and posture conditions apparent to the eye, while dissection of their dead bodies sometimes showed abnormal conditions of liver, kidneys, and other organs. Fully as important was the job of determining how each specific condition, whose counterpart was often found in human beings, could be diminished or even cured by administration of the best vitamin dosages. Stomach tubes were used for some of this work. Injection by needle versus dosage by mouth was also studied in attempts to learn the facts that could be of greatest help in the medical world.

All this work with vitamins throughout the 1940's and, after her appointment as a research associate at the world-famous Sloan-Kettering Institute for Cancer Research, her studies on the effects of cortisones and diet upon the growth of tumors, were leading up to the research work in which Dr. Emerson has found possibly her greatest interest. As a biochemist—and the *bio* means a chemist who studies the effects of chemical substances on living bodies—she became interested in the effects of certain nutritional factors in producing arteriosclerosis (hardening of the arteries) a disease common among older people and one that often hastens their death. She welcomed the opportunity Merck was able to give her to work with rhesus monkeys in trying to learn more about the causes of and cure for this disease, even though rhesus monkeys are vicious little animals, "wild, ferocious little beasts," she calls them, and working with them was not without danger.

Scientists had long been convinced that animals of the monkey family were near enough to the human family in their reactions to foods and susceptibility to nutritional diseases that studies made on monkeys could yield valuable information of benefit to the human race. This be-

lief would be strengthened in the 1950's after scientists
had reported on dietary deficiency studies on Bushman,
the famed gorilla at Chicago's Lincoln Park Zoo who had
died after a seven-month illness at the age of twenty-two.
During his illness he had suffered some of the same types
of senile deterioration that afflict many human beings.
Though his diet had been adequate according to available
standards, he had become overweight and, in his illness,
had developed partial paralysis of one arm and leg, arteriosclerosis, and a form of neuritis known to result from
deficiencies of some of the B vitamins. Autopsies revealed still other conditions in Bushman's body believed
to arise from nutritional deficiencies, despite his pre-
sumably "adequate" diet.

Though gorillas and human beings do not have identical food requirements, scientific studies of Bushman's
body gave scientists like Dr. Emerson additional reason
to believe their nutritional researches in the cause of
arteriosclerosis were on the right track. In the Merck
laboratory they were using dogs and monkeys in this
work, producing hardening of the arteries by deficient
diets and then supplementing those diets with substances
it was hoped would restore the deteriorating blood vessels
to a normal or near normal state. The handling of rhesus
monkeys for such investigations is not an easy or danger-
free task, and Dr. Emerson is truly grateful to her fearless
associates who handle them as her own work is being
done.

To describe a little of how these studies in arteriosclerosis were made: Following work by earlier investigators,
the group at Merck fed fifteen monkeys a B_6-deficient

diet for periods ranging from four to fourteen months. At various periods animals were sacrificed, their bodies studied. Arteries had begun to harden in as early as four months, and other organs were affected. In the first animals killed these diseased conditions could be seen only with a microscope. In animals sacrificed after longer periods, they became visible to the naked eye. Vitamin preparations were then given to live monkeys showing these symptoms and, after certain periods had elapsed and certain dosages had been administered, these animals, too, were sacrificed one by one and examinations were made of their arteries and other organs. By interpretation of messages registered in their bodies, showing the effects of scientifically conducted experiments in feeding them, these animals furnished information it was hoped could bring beneficial results in treating human illnesses. The interest that Merck executives have in this type of research may be gathered from the fact that experimental animals are sometimes given the names of Merck vice-presidents, and it is considered a compliment to have a monkey so named.

When an attractive offer came for Dr. Emerson to return to the University of California in 1956, she was unhappy at the thought of leaving her researches, especially in arteriosclerosis. The new opportunity, as stated earlier, was that of becoming chairman of the Department of Home Economics on the University's Los Angeles campus, or "UCLA," as it is called. In speaking of this opportunity, Dr. Emerson is quick to point out that she has no outstanding qualifications as a teacher. With UCLA's more than 16,000 full-time students the new position would be largely administrative, which appealed to her. Also, she was assured she could serve as a consultant to Merck. When Merck offered to present the university with twenty-nine monkeys to enable Dr. Emerson to continue her researches in California, the opportunity proved irresistible. A few months after she arrived, incidentally, the university's nursery school asked for one of the monkeys as a pet for the children. She realized how far academic life may be removed from a scientist's laboratory, for it was already proving difficult to find someone willing to take care of these far from petlike little animals.

Gladys Emerson was still on the sunny side of her middle fifties when she settled into her new home in California. Behind her lay almost a hundred publications in scientific journals giving results of her work or, as is more usual in scientific research, of work done in collaboration with others. With her was the Garvan Gold Medal to which, in the estimation of her peers, that work had entitled her. Ahead of her were many hopes, including the hope to co-operate with the World Health Organization, UNICEF, and other organizations in finding ways and means to provide better nutrition for parts of the world now seriously underfed. Projects aimed at this end are already underway, and she is actively interested in the Los Angeles World Affairs Council as well as working with UCLA groups.

Dr. Emerson believes with considerable vigor that women do not lack opportunities in chemistry. Ability and a good education are requirements for advancement and, after that, "Work and don't gripe" is her recipe.

This terse advice does not make her unpopular with her fellow women chemists, for she is one of the small group they have honored with the presidency of their honorary fraternity, Iota Sigma Pi.

Whatever her future is to be, her friends say it will not all be work. One of the first things she did in Los Angeles was to get herself a dog—this one a chocolate-fudge-colored miniature poodle. She was soon helping organize a group to sing folk songs together and play all kinds of instruments from pianos and guitars to accordions and recorders. She was quick to discover how much she is able to enjoy football games again—an early love that had long been neglected. These and other pleasures, including travel, are on her schedule for the years ahead, as well as contacts with friends who find her as agreeable a companion outside the laboratory as do those privileged to work with her inside a laboratory.

DOROTHEA RUDNICK

(1907–   )

●◦●

Embryologist whose mastery of delicate techniques for transplanting embryo sections is helping to reveal unknown factors in growth and development

DOROTHEA RUDNICK (pronounced Rood-nik) crowded a lot into her teen-age years, including a strong resistance to the study of science, especially laboratory science. The story of her life between the ages of zero and nineteen indicates that, of all the things she might have chosen to become, a scientist was not one of them.

Life as a separate entity began for her in a private sanitarium in Oconomowoc, Wisconsin, which her Chicago mother favored as a birthplace for the young Rudnicks. With one brother preceding and another following her, it became her lot to grow up between two incipient physicists in the home of a full-fledged chemist father. To use her words, "I grew up in a home where we breathed an analytical atmosphere."

From her point of view this was nothing to be unhappy

156

about. To an intelligent child it soon became obvious that both science and an analytical attitude were interesting. Yet something arose in her young mind to make her resist vigorously any idea that science might be interesting enough to become her own lifework. Too many other possibilities offered themselves—though, frankly, she did not know which of them appealed to her as a life long occupation.

With her brothers Dorothea attended public schools on Chicago's South Side, on her way to Parker High. Parker was a good high school, a fact she still remembers with gratitude for those who made it so. With very few exceptions its teachers had the respect of the student body, even of its least studious members. "As I look back on it, I am impressed by the number of men and women on the faculty who were real personalities, dedicated teachers. They expected us to work and most of us did."

Parker High gave students a degree of choice in what they studied to earn its diploma, and by the time she became a teen-ager Dorothea had some very definite ideas about what she did and did not want to study. History and languages were her main interests, and she chose these studies as often as possible. She took trigonometry because "My older brother said, 'Be sure to take trig. It's fun,' and he was right. I took trig and it was fun." She did not want to take either chemistry or physics, and since Parker High did not require either for its diploma and she could enter the University of Chicago without them, both these subjects were put into the science discard quite happily—a procedure she does not recommend for high-school girls today. With high marks and no science except a little nonlaboratory physiology and some physiography, which she found quite interesting, she graduated from high school in the spring of 1922.

In addition to the fact that science was in the discard, several other facts are clear about this dark-eyed, darkhaired, slenderly built fifteen-year-old who was about to become a freshman at the University of Chicago. First of all, she had been galloping along intellectually at a faster clip than the majority of her fellow students. Also, she was a young person who was not fitting too easily into the pattern imposed by her family and followed unquestioningly by most of the young people in her social, financial, and intellectual group. Going to college was not what Dorothea Rudnick wanted to do most. Going to Europe for a year was her first choice. This was not possible, and she could understand the reasons why. She knew how young she was, even though fifteen and a half seemed older to her that summer than it would ever seem again. She felt in her mind and heart that she had no right to ask for the money a year in Europe would take because higher education for the younger generation of Rudnicks would be an expensive affair for her parents for many years, and a chemist in the Armour Laboratories would never be a rich man. So she made herself as content as she could with opportunities at the University of Chicago as she began to work for her Bachelor of Philosophy degree with a major in languages.

The languages were mainly French and Italian, though German was the language her grandparents had brought with them from their native land. She enjoyed university work. A totally unexpected interest and pleasure came to her from a course in geology. "I'm glad Chicago did not let me do all the choosing," she says, "for I would have missed geology if it had not been a requirement on the way to my Ph.B." College was not a bore, by any means. Nevertheless, after two years of it she quit. She was seventeen and a half that summer—old enough for a job—and she wanted to earn money of her own. By working and saving for a year, she could finance a year abroad, which had been her first choice all along.

Finding a job in Chicago in 1924 was not difficult. A bank located in a down-town skyscraper employed her as a bookkeeper; running an adding machine and sorting checks required little from a girl who had found trigonometry fun. Her parents co-operated by letting her save what she earned. She had made a friend at the university whose family would be living abroad that next year, so Dorothea and she planned to travel together for a period. Together, and at times joining up with the friend's family, they would do some of the things all of them wanted to do—see certain sights in Italy, for example, and hear music in Austria. But Dorothea definitely planned to be on her own, even without her friend, for a good part of the time.

So at eighteen this independent young woman was on her way to Europe, her own money paying for it, the University of Chicago and the job at the bank both happily behind her. It was a glorious adventure to be embarking upon. She was doing what she wanted to do most, at a time when she was young enough to enjoy the pleasures and thrills to their extravagant fullest—even the frights and difficulties, if they came—with the knowledge that she had earned them herself. This latter fact was of importance to her—that she had earned them herself. With the analytical atmosphere behind her (except for the part she had absorbed into her being), she was approaching Europe with an emotional drive that was destined to outlast her money, but not until she had seen and done many of the things she wanted to see and do, including some mountain climbing in the Tyrol and going to Paris, alone, in time to meet the spring and live there for a few months on her own.

All of it was done as inexpensively as possible so that it might last as long as possible. "In Paris I allowed myself ten dollars a week," she says, "and actually I was rich. Most of the people I came to know there had only five dollars a week." By economizing she was able to hold out for a year and a half. Toward the end she borrowed a little, "Not much, though—and I paid it all back," from her parents, for whom friends must surely have been feeling some sympathy while Dorothea's wonderful experiences were occurring. For where are the parents who would not worry a bit about a daughter, off seeing the world on her own at eighteen? But the end did come and, by financial necessity, she was back in Chicago in the midst of the second winter after she had left it.

She now spent some admittedly unhappy months. Facts were facts, and she knew she had to decide what kind of future she should prepare for. If she could have gone out and gotten a writing job, possibly she would have done that. But, as Florence van Straten (*see* p. 126) had come to realize before making decisions that led her into meteorology, "You can't just decide to be a writer, study it a few years and then make a living at it." So Dorothea Rudnick, trying to understand the unfocused drive within her, finally came to the conclusion that it was going to be science of one kind or another and wished she had recognized it earlier.

By this time she had learned at least one thing about herself. "I knew I could not live on secondhand experience alone. Bookish though my tastes were—possibly in part through these tastes that had kept me reading at the British Museum and Bibliothèque Nationale for so many hours when I was following my own inclinations abroad—I had finally recognized that I needed the firsthand experience a laboratory would provide for me." So she made her decision to go back to the university in the fall, continue her major in languages, but take some science courses—probably biology, though the specific subject did not matter much at the moment.

Along with this decision she made another that was not so difficult. No matter what she studied, she was going to have a good time. There can be a little doubt that Miss Rudnick was emerging from her teens as a young person with initiative, with capabilities, a sense of personal responsibility, and a need to get herself focused if she were to develop her potentialities.

What happened soon was unexpected and somewhat electrifying. In a basic course in zoology she became interested in the variety of structural patterns found in the animal kingdom. To her mind ("It is a basically historical mind," she says) embryology—the study of the development of these forms—seemed to be their most important aspect. So she signed up for a course in embryology and in it discovered that intellectual and technical tools were at hand for *analyzing* the life history of animal forms. With this realization her indecision was at an end. Embryos became beautiful and mysterious objects which, properly questioned, might share their secrets, and a student working with her teacher, Professor B. H. Willier, might hope to learn how to ask the right questions. In short, "Embryology fascinated me. It still does." It became a "must" to her.

As would be expected by anyone familiar with her life up to this point, she worked vigorously and progressed speedily. With her Ph.B. in languages, and Phi Beta Kappa in 1928, she did not apply for a fellowship for graduate work because she knew other students had financial needs greater than hers. When her first year in the graduate school taught her she would have greater opportunities with a fellowship, she applied for and held fellowships for her remaining two years at Chicago.

In Professor Willier's section of the Department of Zoology she soon found the special problem, or set of problems, within embryology which has remained her primary interest ever since—differentiation, it is called. To explain: Embryological studies deal with animals in their embryo stage, which lasts in human organisms for the first three months after conception and in other animals for shorter (or longer) periods. In Miss Rudnick's course in embryology students had studied the structure of animals with the idea of following a *process* of development. Differentiation is one aspect of this process, and she became interested in learning what caused one tiny part, or parts, of an embryo to develop into a lung, another into a right ear or tail feather, and in trying to ascertain the time element and sequence of events as they did so.

For example: When she looked at an egg—that favored tool of young embryologists—she knew that if it were a fertilized egg it could, with proper care, develop into a baby chick. When she looked at that same egg after it had been broken into a dish, she knew the yellow part was stored food on which the embryo and baby chick would have fed had the egg been put in an incubator instead of broken into a dish. It was the little white spot that always manages to be on top of the yolk when an egg is poured out of its shell that interested her. This was the living protoplasm, with innate power to become the living animal that pecks its way out of an eggshell. She knew that tiny blob of living protoplasm contained invisibles that would develop into each and every differentiated organ, tissue, bone and other body part of a full-fledged feathery baby chick. Exactly where, she wondered, was the specific something-or-other in that tiny blob of living protoplasm that would develop into the chick's gizzard, or left eyelid or curved talon on its right foot. More important still, what caused each tiny something-or-other to develop physically as it did, when did the process start, and how did it proceed?

If that idea seems fantastically far fetched, surely it is not any more far fetched than an early investigation she undertook at Dr. Willier's suggestion, when she set out to learn the origin of a chick's thyroid. Brought to completion and reported in the Proceedings of the Society for Experimental Biology and Medicine during her second year of graduate study, this investigation "indicated rather clearly" that the tissues which eventually develop into thyroid in a baby chick have their origin in two specific areas (whose location she makes clear to an understanding reader) in the living protoplasm (or blastoderm) at which she had so often looked with a desire to unravel some of its secrets.

Early in her graduate school work she began to develop the delicate techniques for transplanting selected bits of one embryo to another which have brought distinction to her work in differentiation. The technique was not original with her, but it is one only a limited number of embryologists and geneticists can use successfully because of the high degree of manual dexterity it requires. It can be described graphically, and with advantage for a layman reader, by skipping over some of the years that followed the award of her doctorate at the University of Chicago in 1931 and picking her work up after she had reached Albertus Magnus College in New Haven, where she became an assistant professor of zoology in 1940. Those years had been marked by a succession of fellowships that had given her three years of experimental research at the Osborn Zoological Laboratory at Yale and another three years at the University of Rochester before she took her first salaried position as an instructor at the Storrs Agricultural Experiment Station in Connecticut and her second one, briefly, at Wellesley.

Throughout these years Dr. Rudnick had kept up her research work—though on more limited time after her teaching began—that aimed to learn more about how, why, and when things happened in embryos. One of her methods was to transplant parts of one embryo onto another embryo and determine, by careful analyses, what happened and when. In the summer of 1942 she was ready for a research that would attempt to answer two questions, the first of which was: Can the part of a very young embryo that would form a limb in the normal course of development form that same sort of limb if removed and transplanted to another embryo? This type of experiment with chick embryos may be compared, in biological principle, with those made on trees, in which the limb of a Baldwin apple tree is grafted to the trunk of a McIntosh apple tree and produces Baldwin apples on it.

For her experiment Dr. Rudnick chose eggs of White Leghorn chickens as host embryos into which she would transplant selected segments from embryos obtained from eggs of Creepers, a breed of short-legged chickens. When bred to one another, Creepers produce eggs of which one-fourth are unable to hatch. This percentage of their embryos die in the shell and, of that fourth, those that live long enough to develop legs at all have extremely short stumpy ones, not just short ones.

The experiment was performed at the Storrs Laboratories, where she had worked earlier and to which she was welcome to return. White Leghorn eggs chosen as hosts were submitted to approximately sixty hours of incubation while the Creeper eggs were submitted to only twenty-four to thirty hours of incubation. Each White Leghorn egg used in the research was held up to a light that revealed where its embryo was situated and the spot marked on the shell. With a tiny saw Dr. Rudnick sawed a small window in the shell around this spot and left the window in its place, ready for removal later. Then, in a Petri dish containing a warm salt solution she broke one of the donor eggs. Using her binocular dissecting microscope she freed its embryo (or blastoderm) from the yolk and flattened it with repeated floodings of the salt solution blown from a glass pipette.

With a glass needle (made by pulling out a bit of glass rod in a very tiny gas flame) she severed a segment from the right and another from the left of the *sinus rhomboidalis* situated in the flattened embryo's center, including but larger than the limb-forming area. (At this early incubation stage it is impossible to excise and transplant a single limb-forming segment with success.) She then removed the window from the first egg, tore the underlying membrane for a distance and secured it with tiny forceps, focused the light of her microscope upon the embryo beneath the open window, cut a tiny slit in the flank of the host embryo, sucked up in her glass pipette the first segment of the readied embryo (the other segment would be placed in a second Leghorn embryo) and, working under the microscope, tucked the graft into the slit in the body cavity of the host. Then the window was replaced in the shell, sealed with paraffin and the egg returned to its incubator.

The complete operation required ten to fifteen minutes and "It's not very difficult," she says—a statement that needs to be understood as one understands such a statement from an artist as he shows you an etching he has made. From the perfection of her delicate techniques Dorothea Rudnick derives an esthetic satisfaction that makes her somewhat oblivious to difficulties.

If not difficult (for her!) it must surely be tedious to carry out such a research satisfactorily because so many eggs must be worked with. Though her paper in *The Journal of Experimental Zoology* in 1945 reporting on the experiment just described does not reveal how many eggs were used in it, it does say there were 159 individual operations in which the host embryo was living when examination was made of them in from six to fourteen days after transplantation had taken place. Of the 159 living embryos, 93 bore grafts, with nearly one-third of them showing recognizable leg or wing parts, growing from practically any region of the White Leghorn embryo.

Examination of the limb grafts showed that the answer to the first question she had set out to answer was affirmative. Transplanted to another embryo, the same sort of limb would grow that would have developed in the original embryo.

The second question was answered, too. This one was: Is the abnormality due to something *within* the limb-forming area or, as some scientists were suggesting, due to some thing that comes from outside that area, such as poor circulation or some poison in the blood that circulates as the limb bud takes shape? To find her answer to this, she had taken donor grafts of limb areas from embryos at an age before they had a circulatory system of their own. They had never been exposed to any but a normal blood circulation. When examinations revealed that in one-fourth of the successful transplants the grafts showed legs of the extremely short stumpy variety—*the same percentage* that develop (but die in the shell) when

Creeper bred to Creeper eggs are set to hatch normally—the abnormality was shown to be due to something in the limb area itself.

Because of the early incubation stage (twenty-four to thirty hours) at which these grafts had been successfully transplanted, the layman can see at what an early embryonic stage the location of the something-or-other in a tiny blob of living protoplasm that develops into a leg or wing can be recognized. He can see, too, that a prodigious amount of work is involved in research of this nature, which requires so much time for painstaking manual procedures before the further time-consuming examinations and analyses are made which reveal results.

This study of differentiation of prospective limb material had been preceded by other work on chick embryos in which lung, heart, liver, gut, and central nervous systems had been studied. As a Fellow at the Osborn Zoological Laboratory at Yale she had done some earlier work on rat embryos with Dr. J. S. Nicholas in which it was shown that rat embryos, removed and transplanted to tissue cultures outside the animal body, could go through part of their development (form beating hearts, etc.) outside the mother's body. In one of these experiments one hundred successful transplants were performed and their results reported on. For the most part, though, Dr. Rudnick's interests centered steadily on chick embryos, and the Guggenheim Award she received in the early 1950's enabled her to devote most of a year, freed from teaching and administrative duties at Albertus Magnus, where she had become a full professor in 1948, to further studies with these embryos.

The specific research for which the Guggenheim was granted was on enzyme systems associated with the synthesis of protein in the chick embryo. This was an extension or an earlier interest in differentiation of the liver, the center of protein synthesis in the adult animal. Now she wanted to study enzymatic activities concerned with getting the synthesis of the protein started as it was transferred from the egg yolk into the living embryo and used as body building material there. How early, she wanted to know, can the associated enzymes be detected in an embryonic liver?

The work was done with two coworkers, Drs. Mela and Waelsch, in the laboratory of the latter, and Dr. Rudnick found it an interesting adventure for an embryologist to be invited into a biochemical laboratory to learn the very sophisticated methods of studying enzymes there. They succeeded in outlining the main features of the history of the enzyme they were studying, finding it appears first outside the embryo proper, in the membrane covering of the egg yolk. Later, after the embryonic liver had appeared, it was found there, and considerably later, in the brain.

This led quite naturally to Dr. Rudnick's desire to study more specifically the tissues of the nervous system (brain and spinal cord) of the chick, and she and Dr. Waelsch embarked upon this study later. Some of it is still under way in 1959. But before embarking upon it, Dr. Rudnick finished her Guggenheim Award year with four or five months abroad, where she visited laboratories to see and learn about embryological work as carried on in Europe. She worked for six weeks in Etienne Wolff's laboratory in Strasbourg, and gave a seminar in Bologna in Italian, "With much coaching," she adds.

Dr. Rudnick is one of the scientists who derive satisfactions from both teaching and research and her situation in New Haven gives her opportunity for both. Her classroom and laboratory at Albertus Magnus College are but a few minutes' drive from the Osborn Zoological Laboratory at Yale, where she has a small laboratory in which she carries on her research work as it can be done with Osborn's facilities available to her. This is done for the most part over week ends and during summer and other vacations, for her teaching schedule is heavy. When an experiment or research requires it, however, she is at Osborn for an evening's or late afternoon's work.

Albertus Magnus is a small college with only a few hundred students—all of them women. Its resources for science studies are necessarily limited. The caliber of the work it offers in biology may be judged by the fact that in the college year ending in the spring of 1958, two of its seven zoology majors received scholarships for graduate work, one at Yale and the other at Columbia.

In addition to her research and teaching Dr. Rudnick has served for some years as editor of the volume published annually by the Society for the Study of Growth and Development which contains the papers presented at the symposium it fosters each year. She still enjoys writing and has contributed to textbooks and other publications. She is a recognized authority in her field of embryology, with the possibility of years of good work ahead of her, during which, she feels absolutely certain, embryology will continue to fascinate her.

INDEX